PROBLEM SOLVING: GRADES 5-6
TABLE OF CONTENTS

UNIT	STRATEGY	

Unit I: Whole Numbers

Unit II: Fractions

Unit III: Improper Fractions and Mixed Numbers

Unit IV: Multiplying Fractions

Unit V: Dividing Fractions

INTRODUCTION

The National Council of Teachers of Mathematics (NCTM) has set specific standards to help students become confident of their mathematical abilities. Communicating mathematically and problem solving are the keys to helping students develop skills to apply in their daily lives and in later careers.

Based on the belief that students learn to reason mathematically in order to become problem-solvers, the strategies in this book show students more than one way to solve problems. These strategies are not absolute techniques, however. Learning a multitude of ways to approach a problem is part of the philosophy in developing sets of problem-solving strategies.

ORGANIZATION

The chapters offer several strategies to solve a given type of problem: Whole Numbers, Fractions, Improper Fractions and Mixed Numbers, Multiplying Fractions, Dividing Fractions, Decimals, Ratios and Percentages, Probability, Geometry, and Pre-Algebra.

SPECIAL FEATURE

Each chapter concludes with a "Math Madness" activity page that presents an opportunity for students to choose their own strategy to solve problems. The character Harriet the Handy Woman is featured on each of these pages. Harriet provides the students with a unique way to approach the challenges. Divergent thinking is promoted in these lessons.

PROBLEM SOLVING STRATEGIES

The following Problem Solving Strategies are demonstrated:

CHOOSE AN OPERATION Students determine which operation (addition, subtraction, multiplication, or division) to use based on the information presented.

ESTIMATION Students learn both when and how to estimate answers, based on rounding numbers and performing the appropriate operation. Estimation is encouraged as a strategy in all problem solving to verify reasonableness of answers.

FIND A PATTERN This strategy emphasizes pattern recognition of given sequences of numbers, geometric shapes, pictorial information, and other data for problem solving.

GUESS AND CHECK Students learn a variety of methods to reduce the number of trial and error efforts needed to reach accuracy in answers.

IDENTIFY EXTRA OR MISSING INFORMATION By identifying pertinent information, students learn to recognize information which is extra or missing.

MAKE/USE A DRAWING Creating visual images of information makes analysis of the facts easier.

USE EQUALITY/INEQUALITY Students develop strategies to compare fractions for concept development.

MAKE A TABLE Pattern recognition, identification of extra or missing information, and arrangement of data into a visual form demonstrate the effectiveness of making a table.

USE A GRAPH Graphing organizes information so that comparisons can be made visually.

MULTI-STEP PROBLEMS Some complex problems require the completion of more than one step to calculate the solution. This strategy emphasizes the importance of identifying both the given information and the order of operations to reach the solution.

USE LOGIC As it implies, using logic is similar to using common sense. In this strategy students learn to recognize relationships and to answer the question, "Does it make sense?" Strategies include a process of elimination of answers and visual representation of information to organize the elements of a problem.

WORK BACKWARDS This section introduces a strategy for solving complex problems in which the end result is given. By recognizing clue words and using them to solve the problem, students can work backwards from an answer. This skill develops background for later success in algebra.

WRITE A NUMBER SENTENCE Converting written statements into numerical sentences to solve for an unknown is the basis of an algebraic approach. This strategy demonstrates identification of known and unknown information to develop sentences for solutions.

DEFINE MATHEMATICAL TERMS Relating mathematical language and representing symbolism in a variety of ways are extended in problem solving strategies.

USE

This book is designed for independent use by students who have had instruction in the specific skills covered in these lessons. Copies of the activities can be given to individuals, pairs of students, or small groups for completion. They can also be used as a center activity. If students are familiar with the content, the worksheets can be homework for reviewing and reinforcing problem-solving concepts.

To begin, determine the implementation that fits your students' needs and your classroom structure. The following plan suggests a format for this implementation:

1. <u>Explain</u> the purpose of the worksheets to your class.
2. <u>Review</u> the mechanics of how you want students to work with the exercises.
3. <u>Review</u> the specific skill for the students who may not remember the process for successful completion of the computation.
4. <u>Introduce</u> students to the process and to the purpose of the activities. Distribute the Letter to Students.
5. <u>Do</u> a practice activity together.
6. <u>Allow</u> students to experiment, discover, and explore a variety of ways to solve a given problem.

Additional Notes

1. <u>Parent Communication</u>. Send the Letter to Parents home with students, and encourage students to share the Letter to Students with their parents.
2. <u>Bulletin Board</u>. Display completed worksheets to show student progress.
3. <u>Center Activities</u>. Use the worksheets as center activities to give students the opportunity to work cooperatively.
4. <u>Class Record</u>. Duplicate the grid sheets found on pages 7–9. Record student names in the left column. Note date of completion of each lesson for each student.
5. <u>Have fun</u>. Working with these activities can be fun as well as meaningful for you and your students.

Dear Parent,

During this school year, our class will be working with mathematical problem solving strategies. To increase your child's problem solving skills, we will be completing activity sheets that provide practice to ensure mastery of these important skills.

From time to time, I may send home activity sheets. To best help your child, please consider the following suggestions:

- Provide a quiet place to work.
- Go over the directions and the sample exercises together.
- Encourage your child to do his or her best.
- Check the lesson when it is complete.
- Go over your child's work, and note improvements as well as concerns.

Help your child maintain a positive attitude about problem solving activities. Let your child know that each lesson provides an opportunity to have fun and to learn. If your child expresses anxiety about these strategies, help him or her understand what causes the stress. Then talk about ways to eliminate math anxiety.

Above all, enjoy this time you spend with your child. He or she will feel your support, and skills will improve with each activity completed.

Thank you for your help!

Cordially,

© Steck-Vaughn Company

Name _____ Date _____

Dear Student:

   This year you will be working with problem solving strategies in mathematics. You're wondering how well you'll do. Math problem solving is an important skill, and sometimes people feel anxious if they don't understand right away. The activities will help you practice so you can feel more confident about working math problems. You will be reviewing many strategies with sample problems and working some word problems on your own. These activities will show you a fun way to learn problem solving.

As you complete the worksheets, remember the following:
- Read the directions carefully.
- Study the sample problems, and follow the steps for each strategy.
- Read each question carefully.
- Check your answers after you complete a problem.

   You will learn many ways to solve math problems. Have fun as you develop these skills!

STUDENT NAME	CHAPTER 1								CHAPTER 2								CHAPTER 3								CHAPTER 4							
	1	2	3	4	5	6	7	8	1	2	3	4	5	6	7	8	1	2	3	4	5	6	7	8	1	2	3	4	5	6	7	8

© Steck-Vaughn Company

Problem Solving 5-6, SV 6761-1

STUDENT NAME	CHAPTER 5								CHAPTER 6								CHAPTER 7								CHAPTER 8							
	1	2	3	4	5	6	7	8	1	2	3	4	5	6	7	8	1	2	3	4	5	6	7	8	1	2	3	4	5	6	7	8

STUDENT NAME	CHAPTER 9								CHAPTER 10								COMMENTS
	1	2	3	4	5	6	7	8	1	2	3	4	5	6	7	8	

Correlation to the NCTM Standards for grades 5 - 8

These charts indicate the specific mathematics skills incorporated in the activities in this guide correlated to the National Council for Teachers of Mathematics (NCTM) Standards for grades 5 - 8.

	Unit 1	Unit 2	Unit 3	Unit 4	Unit 5	Unit 6	Unit 7	Unit 8	Unit 9	Unit 10
MATHEMATICS AS PROBLEM SOLVING										
Use problem-solving approach . . .	X	X	X	X	X	X	X	X	X	X
Formulate problems . . .										
Develop and apply a variety . . .	X	X	X	X	X	X	X	X	X	X
Verify and interpret results . . .	X	X	X	X	X	X	X	X	X	X
Generalize solutions . . .							X			
Acquire confidence . . .										
MATHEMATICS AS COMMUNICATION										
Model situations . . .	X	X	X	X	X	X	X	X	X	X
Reflect on and clarify their own thinking . . .		X	X	X	X	X	X	X	X	X
Develop common understandings . . .	X	X	X	X	X	X	X	X	X	X
Use the skills of reading, listening, and viewing . . .	X	X	X	X	X	X	X	X	X	X
Discuss mathematical ideas . . .	X	X	X	X	X	X	X	X	X	X
Appreciate the value . . .		X	X	X	X	X	X	X	X	X
MATHEMATICS AS REASONING										
Recognize and apply deductive and inductive . . .	X		X	X			X			
Understand and apply reasoning . . .	X		X					X		
Make and evaluate . . .										
Validate their own thinking . . .										
Appreciate the pervasive use . . .										
MATHEMATICAL CONNECTIONS										
See mathematics . . .										
Explore problem . . .	X	X	X	X	X	X	X	X	X	X
Use a mathematical idea . . .	X									
Apply mathematical thinking . . .	X		X							
Value the role of mathematics . . .										
NUMBERS & NUMBER RELATIONSHIPS										
Understand, represent, and use . . .	X	X	X	X	X	X	X	X	X	X
Develop number sense . . .	X	X	X	X	X	X	X	X	X	X
Understand and apply . . .	X	X	X	X	X	X	X	X	X	X
Investigate relationships . . .	X	X	X	X	X	X	X	X	X	X
Represent numerical relationships . . .	X	X	X	X	X	X	X	X	X	X
NUMBER SYSTEMS & NUMBER THEORY										
Understand and appreciate . . .	X	X	X	X	X	X	X	X	X	X
Develop and use order relations . . .	X	X	X	X	X	X	X	X	X	X
Extend their understanding . . .	X	X	X	X	X	X	X	X	X	X
Understand how the basic . . .	X	X	X	X	X	X	X	X	X	X
Develop and apply number theory . . .	X	X	X	X	X	X	X	X	X	X
COMPUTATION & ESTIMATION										
Compute with whole numbers . . .	X	X	X	X	X	X	X	X	X	X
Develop, analyze, and explain procedures . . .	X	X	X	X	X	X	X	X	X	X
Develop, analyze, and explain methods . . .	X	X	X	X	X	X	X	X	X	X
Select and use an appropriate method . . .	X	X	X	X	X	X	X	X	X	X
Use computation, estimation, and proportions . . .	X	X	X	X	X	X	X	X	X	X
Use estimation to check . . .	X				X					

Standard labels (left margin): STANDARD 1, STANDARD 2, STANDARD 3, STANDARD 4, STANDARD 5, STANDARD 6, STANDARD 7

Problem Solving 5-6, SV 6761-1

Correlation to the NCTM Standards for grades 5 - 8 (continued)

	Unit 1	Unit 2	Unit 3	Unit 4	Unit 5	Unit 6	Unit 7	Unit 8	Unit 9	Unit 10
PATTERNS & FUNCTIONS (STANDARD 8)										
Describe, extend, analyze, and create . . .				X	X	X	X			
Describe and represent relationships . . .					X	X	X			
Analyze functional relationships . . .				X	X	X	X			
Use patterns and functions . . .				X	X	X	X			
ALGEBRA (STANDARD 9)										
Understand algebraic concepts . . .							X	X	X	X
Represent situations and number patterns . . .							X	X	X	X
Analyze tables and graphs . . .	X	X					X	X		
Develop confidence in solving . . .										X
Investigate inequalities . . .										X
Apply algebraic methods to solve . . .									X	X
STATISTICS (STANDARD 10)										
Systematically collect, organize, and describe . . .										
Construct, read, and interpret . . .	X						X			
Make inferences and convincing arguments . . .										
Evaluate arguments . . .										
Develop an appreciation . . .										
PROBABILITY (STANDARD 11)										
Model situations by devising . . .										
Model situations by constructing . . .										
Appreciate the power of using . . .								X		
Make predictions . . .								X		
Develop an appreciation . . .								X		
GEOMETRY (STANDARD 12)										
Identify, describe, compare, and classify . . .									X	
Visualize and represent geometric figures . . .									X	
Explore transformation . . .										
Represent and solve problems . . .									X	
Understand and apply geometric properties . . .									X	
Develop an appreciation of geometry . . .									X	
MEASUREMENT (STANDARD 13)										
Extend their understanding . . .									X	
Estimate, make, and use measurements . . .									X	
Select appropriate units and tools . . .										
Understand the structure . . .										
Extend their understanding . . .										
Develop the concepts of rates . . .										
Develop formulas and procedures . . .									X	

Name _____ Date _____

ASSESSMENT, page 1

Follow the directions to solve each problem.

Estimate the answer by rounding numbers to the nearest hundreds.
The problem may have more than 1 step.

1. Altogether, the rock star's jacket has 3,433 glittery spangles. The collar has 838 spangles. The sleeves have 624 spangles. About how many spangles are on the rest of the jacket? _____

Work backwards to solve this problem.

2. Tanya wanted to fill her scrapbook with picture postcards. The scrapbook had 16 pages, and each page held 6 postcards. In 1 town she bought 13 postcards, in another she bought 28 postcards, and in the last town she bought 34 postcards. Did Tanya buy enough postcards to fill her scrapbook? _____

Change the fractions into equivalent fractions to solve this problem.

3. Tyler, Megan, and Janna were in the rope-climbing contest. Tyler climbed $\frac{7}{12}$ of the way up the rope, Megan climbed $\frac{5}{6}$ of the way, and Janna climbed $\frac{2}{3}$ of the way. Who won the contest? _____

Make a plan and choose the correct operations to solve this problem.
The problem has more than 1 step.

4. Camela decides to make a pair of pajamas for her dog Fido. She needs $\frac{7}{8}$ of a yard of fabric. She has 1 piece that is $\frac{1}{3}$ of a yard, another piece that is $\frac{1}{4}$ of a yard, and a third piece that is $\frac{5}{12}$ of a yard. Does she have enough fabric to make Fido's pajamas? _____

Write a number sentence to help you solve this problem. Reduce your answer if possible.

5. Each day Thom had to write in the ship log. On the first day he wrote $\frac{3}{4}$ page. On the second day he wrote $\frac{7}{8}$ page. On the third day he wrote $\frac{1}{2}$ page. How many pages did he write altogether? _____

Use guessing and checking to solve this problem.

6. One time Carri was able to drive $6\frac{1}{2}$ laps before she ran out of gas. Today she only went $\frac{2}{3}$ that far before she ran out of gas. How many laps did Carri drive today before she ran out of gas? _____

Name _____ Date _____

ASSESSMENT, page 2

Use the graph and logic to help you solve this problem.

7. What fraction of the flour is used to make
   both the pepperoni and olive pizzas?

   _____

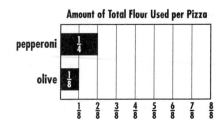

Make a drawing to help you solve the problem.

8. For a snack, the 3 candy stripers ate $3\frac{3}{4}$ ounces of carrots. If they shared the
   carrots equally, how many ounces of carrots did each candy striper eat?

   _____

Cross out the extra facts. Then solve the problem.

9. Greg brought goulash to the party. He used $3\frac{3}{4}$ cups of gravy in his goulash. His
   recipe makes $10\frac{1}{2}$ large servings. If he divides each serving by $\frac{1}{2}$, how many
   smaller servings will he have? _____

Solve the problem using a decimal point.

10. The zoo has 1,000 birds in the bird house. The birds eat 675.75 pounds of seed
    in a week. If each bird eats the same amount, how much seed would 1 bird eat
    in a week? _____

Choose an operation to solve the problem.

11. Guests at the party drank chocolate milk. Each pitcher held 38 ounces.
    If 12 guests each drank 9.5 ounces of milk, how many pitchers of milk did
    they drink? _____

Make a ratio table to help you solve these problems.

12. Ned went to the video arcade. It costs Ned $1.00 to play 2 games. How much
    would it cost Ned to play 10 games? _____

13. Oranges are on sale at 2 pounds for $0.90. Is this equal to 3 pounds of oranges
    for $1.35? _____

ASSESSMENT, page 3

Use a formula and proportions to help you solve this problem.

14. Stu is 6 feet tall. He is standing by a tree. His shadow is 4 feet long.
The tree's shadow is 12 feet long. How tall is the tree? _____

Use the table below to solve this problem. Reduce your answer if possible.

15. Lucy did a survey. She asked her classmates what
color backpack they had. She put results in a
frequency table. There are 30 students in Lucy's
class, so there are 30 possible outcomes.

What is the probability that Shenille has a green
or a black backpack?

_____

Color	Number of students
blue	8
red	5
black	4
green	7
gray	6

Write a number sentence to help you solve this problem.

16. Sal had 45 hits in 180 at-bats. What is his batting average? _____

Use a formula to solve this problem. To find the area of a circle, the formula is A = π x r².

17. A small pizza has a diameter of 8 inches. A large pizza has a diameter of
14 inches. What is the difference in area between the large pizza and the
small pizza? _____

**Use a formula to solve this problem. To find the volume of a rectangular box,
use the formula V = W x L x H.**

18. A square box (cube) has a width of 4 inches. What is the volume of the cube?

_____

**Write an equation using addition or subtraction for this problem. Then solve the equation.
(Hint: Let X = the variable.)**

19. Maria has 17 CDs. Of these, 9 are rock music, and the rest are pop music.
How many pop music CDs does Maria have? _____

Write an inequality and then solve the problem.

20. Together Nick and Raul scored more than 40 points in a basketball game.
Nick scored 6 more points than Raul. How many points might Raul have scored?
(Hint: Let X = Raul's score.) _____

Name _____ Date _____

HEAVY METAL LIVES!

You can solve some problems by estimating the answers. An estimate is found by rounding some or all of the numbers, then finding the answer by doing mental math. You can use a calculator to check your answers.

 STEP 1 **Read the problem.**
Leonita's school sponsored a rock concert. The auditorium has 302 seats. All the seats were sold. The school earned $15.25 on each ticket. About how much money did the school earn?

 STEP 2 **Identify the facts.**
All 302 seats in the auditorium were sold. The school earned $15.25 for each ticket.

 STEP 3 **Round all numbers.**
302 can be rounded to 300. $15.25 can be rounded to $15.

 STEP 4 **Estimate the answer.**
To find the answer, multiply. Try doing mental math. Think of $15 as $10 + $5. First multiply 300 × $10 = $3,000. Then multiply 300 × $5 = $1,500. To find the total, add $3,000 + $1,500 = $4,500. The school made about $4,500.

Now it's your turn! Estimate the answers by rounding numbers to the nearest hundreds. Some of the problems have more than 1 step.

1. Altogether, the rock star's jacket has 3,433 glittery spangles. The collar has 838 spangles. The sleeves have 624 spangles. About how many spangles are on the rest of the jacket?

   _____

2. The concert program has 688 good luck messages. One page holds 92 messages. About how many pages have messages?

   _____

3. The band drove to the concert. The first day they drove 339 miles. The second day they drove 278 miles. The third day they drove 215 miles. About how many miles did they drive altogether?

   _____

4. If the band returns home by the same route, about how many miles will their total round trip be?

   _____

Name _____ Date _____

GET READY!

Sometimes a problem does not tell you to add, subtract, multiply, or divide. Read the problem carefully to choose the correct operation.

 Read the problem.
Mr. Rigman's class is having a party. If each of the 33 students sells 1 ticket for $6, how much money will the class collect?

 Identify the facts.
There are 33 students in the class. Each student will sell 1 ticket. Tickets cost $6 each.

STEP 3 **Choose an operation.**
Although you could add $6 (price of ticket) 33 (number of students) times, it is faster to multiply.

STEP 4

Solve the problem.
$6 a ticket × 33 students = $198
The class will collect $198 from ticket sales.

Now it's your turn! Choose an operation to solve each problem.

1. Angela ordered 429 decorations for the party. If the 33 students in her class share equally, how many decorations will each student get?

_____

2. Other students could trade in 16 soup labels for 1 free ticket to the party. If the class collected 832 soup labels, how many free tickets did they give away?

_____

3. The students made popcorn for the party. Each cup of unpopped popcorn held 228 kernels. They used 142 cups of popcorn. How many kernels of unpopped popcorn did they use?

_____

4. After the party students made donations of gloves and mittens to the needy. If 135 students gave 1,215 pairs of gloves and mittens, how many pairs did each student donate?

_____

ON A WHIRLWIND TOUR!

Some problems use more than 1 operation. You may have to add, subtract, multiply, and divide in any order.

STEP 1 ▷ **Read the problem.**

Raul plans to meet his penpals while on tour with the orchestra. Geoffrey, his English penpal, lives 120 kilometers from London. Raul will drive halfway to meet Geoffrey. He will travel at 30 kph. How long will it take Raul to make the round trip from London?

STEP 2 ▷ **Make a plan.**

To find how many kilometers is halfway, divide.
To find how long it will take Raul to travel that distance, divide.
To find how long it will take Raul to make the round trip, multiply.

STEP 3 ▷ **Solve the problem.**

$\frac{1}{2}$ of 120 kilometers = 120 ÷ 2 = 60 km
60 km ÷ 30 kph = 2 hours
2 hours each way × 2 ways = 4 hours for the round trip
It will take Raul 4 hours to make the round trip.

Now it's your turn! Make a plan to solve each problem.

1. Raul will meet his penpal Hans in Hamburg, Germany. Then he will travel 480 km to rejoin the orchestra. He will leave Hamburg at 8 AM and travel 80 kph to be at the next theater by 3 PM. How much time will the trip take Raul?

   _____

2. Will he get to the theater on time?

   _____

3. Raul had $300 to spend on his trip. He bought a train ticket in England for $48 and a train ticket in Germany for $160. His other expenses amounted to $73. At his last stop he found a souvenir he wanted to buy for $24. Did he have enough money to buy the souvenir?

   _____

4. How much money did Raul have left?

   _____

Name _____ Date _____

WHAT'S YOUR GUESS?

One fast way to solve problems is to guess the answer, then check it. If your guess is not right, try again. Use what you learn from the first guess to make your next guess better. Guess and check until you find the right answer.

 STEP 1 **Read the problem.**
What operations will complete this problem correctly? Write × or ÷ on the lines to complete the problem. Use a calculator to check your answers.

1,896 ____ 79 ____ 2 = 48

 STEP 2 **Solve the problem.**
Use guessing and checking.
Guess: 48 is smaller than 1,896, so divide first.
Check: $1,896 \div 79 = 24$
Guess: 48 is larger than 24, so multiply next.
Check: $24 \times 2 = 48$
Check again: $1,896 \div 79 \times 2 = 48$

Now it's your turn! Use guessing and checking to solve the problems. Work from left to right. Use a calculator to help you solve each problem.

1. Robyn won tickets to the amusement park by solving this puzzle. She had to multiply and divide to find the answer. Can you solve the puzzle?

   675 ____ 33 ____ 75 = 297

2. Fred won 2 tickets to the ball game by working this puzzle. He had to add, subtract, and multiply to get the right answer. Can you work the problem?

   210 ____ 3 ____ 321 ____ 4 = 313

3. If Jeff can solve this problem, he will win a free movie ticket. He knows he must add, subtract, multiply, and divide to find the answer. Help him find the correct order.

   195 ____ 3 ____ 4 ____ 24 ____ 5 = 28

Name _____   Date _____

TOURING THE SOUTHWEST

Sometimes you need to work backwards to solve a problem. Read the problem carefully. Then work backwards to find the answer.

 Read the problem.

Tanya is taking a Southwestern tour. If she writes a 15-page report trip, she will earn extra credit in social studies. So far she has written 148 sentences about Mexican history, 136 sentences about American history, and 128 sentences about the desert. If 30 sentences equal 1 page, how many more sentences must Tanya write to complete her report?

 Work backwards.

To find the number of sentences Tanya has already written, add.
To find the numbers of sentences needed altogether, multiply.
To find the number of sentences Tanya still has to write, subtract.

 Solve the problem.

148 + 136 + 128 = 412 sentences written
30 sentences per page × 15 pages = 450 total sentences needed
450 sentences needed − 412 sentences written = 38
Tanya still needs to write 38 sentences to complete her report.

Now it's your turn! Work backwards to solve these problems.

1. Tanya learned that long ago 11,045 Native Americans had lived in 47 villages. The same number of people lived in each village. Then all but 16 villages vanished. How many people were in the villages that vanished?

   _____

2. How many people were in the villages that remained?

   _____

3. Tanya wanted to fill her scrapbook with picture postcards. The scrapbook had 16 pages, and each page held 6 postcards. In 1 town she bought 13 postcards, in another she bought 28 postcards, and in the last town she bought 34 postcards. Did Tanya buy enough postcards to fill her scrapbook?

   _____

4. How many more postcards did she need?

   _____

ON THE ROAD AGAIN!

A graph is a special table of facts. A bar graph contains information in the shape of bars. To read a bar graph, match the bars with the numbers.

Notice the numbers at the top of the graph below. Then notice the words at the top: Number of tickets sold, in thousands. These words tell you what information the graph contains. The words *in thousands* mean you should multiply the numbers at the top of the graph by 1,000. So, for example, in Tampa 40,000 tickets were sold.

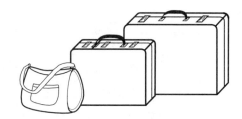

Number of tickets sold, per thousand

Cities	10	20	30	40	50	60	70	80
Anaheim, CA	🎟	🎟	🎟	🎟	🎟	🎟	🎟	
Tampa, FL	🎟	🎟	🎟	🎟				
Cleveland, OH	🎟	🎟	🎟	🎟	🎟	🎟		

STEP 1 ▷ **Read the problem.**

The agent for the rock group Delta wants to know which city had their largest crowd on their last tour. She will include the city again in their next tour. She is considering Anaheim, Tampa, and Cleveland. Which city should she choose?

STEP 2 ▷ **Read the graph.**

Find the city name. Then move your finger across the graph to where the bar ends. Then move your finger to the top of the graph to find the number of tickets sold, in thousands.

STEP 3 ▷ **Write the facts.**

The graph shows that 70,000 tickets were sold in Anaheim; 40,000 tickets were sold in Tampa; and 60,000 tickets were sold in Cleveland.

STEP 4 ▷ **Solve the problem.**

The graph shows that Delta's largest crowd was in Anaheim, so the agent should schedule that city for the next tour.

Name _____ Date _____

ON THE ROAD AGAIN! PART 2

A graph can give all kinds of information. Study the graph below to solve the following problems.

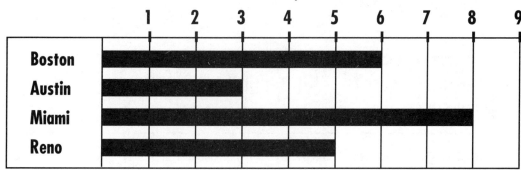

Shirt Sales, in thousands

Cities	1	2	3	4	5	6	7	8	9
Boston									
Austin									
Miami									
Reno									

Now it's your turn! Solve these problems using the graph.

1. The rock group Delta sells T-shirts at each concert. In which city did they sell the most T-shirts?

   _____

2. In which city did they sell the fewest T-shirts?

   _____

3. How many T-shirts did they sell altogether in Boston and Reno?

   _____

4. How many T-shirts did they sell altogether in the 4 cities?

   _____

5. If their T-shirts sell for $11 each, how much money did they earn in Austin?

   _____

6. How much did they earn in Boston?

   _____

7. How much did they earn altogether?

   _____

MATH MADNESS

1

You are a real math magician when you can work complicated problems in your head. Can you work this one in your head?

$$5 \times 32 \times 744 \times 6{,}543 \times 0 \times 91 \times 65 = \underline{\hspace{2cm}}$$

You can also use a calculator to check your answer. Work from left to right. Which way is easier to solve the problem, using your head or using a calculator?

2

Here is a game of 2s. Put in the right operation signs to make each problem work.

a.	2	2	2	2	=	1	_____
b.	2	2	2	2	=	2	_____
c.	2	2	2	2	=	3	_____
d.	2	2	2	2	=	4	_____
e.	2	2	2	2	=	5	_____
f.	2	2	2	2	=	6	_____

3

Now try it with 3s.

a.	3	3	3	3	=	3	_____
b.	3	3	3	3	=	4	_____
c.	3	3	3	3	=	5	_____
d.	3	3	3	3	=	6	_____
e.	3	3	3	3	=	7	_____

Unit I: Whole Numbers

© Steck-Vaughn Company

Problem Solving 5-6, SV 6761-1

Name _____ Date _____

FRACTIONS DEPARTMENT STORE

When solving problems, you sometimes need to work with parts of a whole or parts of a group. Fractions are equal parts of a whole. A drawing can help to show the parts.

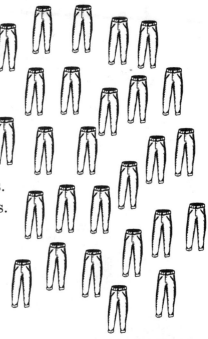

 Read the problem.
The jeans racks at the store are divided into 3 equal sections. Each section is $\frac{1}{3}$ of all the racks. Carmen has 27 pairs of jeans to put on the racks. If she divides the jeans equally among the 3 sections, how many jeans will be in each section?

 Identify the facts.
There are 3 equal sections. There are 27 pairs of jeans. Carmen divides the jeans equally among the 3 sections.

STEP 3 **Solve the problem.**
Separate the jeans into 3 equal groups. Draw a circle around $\frac{1}{3}$ of the jeans in the drawing above.
    27 pairs ÷ 3 = 9
Each section holds 9 pairs, or $\frac{1}{3}$ of all the jeans.

Now it's your turn! Make a drawing to help you solve the problems.

1. Carmen has 4 shelves for shirts. She has 16 shirts to put on the shelves. If she divides the shirts equally among the 4 shelves, how many shirts will she put on each shelf?

   _____

2. What fraction of the shirts will she put on each shelf?

   _____

3. A rich customer buys 10 dresses at the store. She wants Carmen to send an equal number of the dresses to each of 5 friends. How many dresses will Carmen send to each friend?

   _____

4. What fraction of the dresses will each friend receive?

   _____

5. Carmen has room in her department for 30 pairs of shoes. She wants to stock an equal number of sneakers, sandals, and loafers. How many of each kind of shoe can she stock?

   _____

6. What fraction of all the shoes would each kind be?

   _____

Unit II: Fractions
© Steck-Vaughn Company

23

Problem Solving 5-6, SV 6761-1

Name _____   Date _____

BIG TOY SALE!

Sometimes a problem does not tell you to add or subtract. Then you must decide which operation to choose to solve the problem.

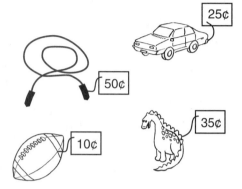

25¢

50¢

35¢

10¢

STEP 1 > **Read the problem.**
During the big sale, toys with red tags are $3.00 off and toys with green tags are $2.00 off. Larry put red tags on $\frac{3}{8}$ of all the toys, and he put green tags on $\frac{1}{8}$ of all the toys. Altogether, what fraction of all the toys are tagged for the sale?

STEP 2 > **Choose an operation.**
To find what fraction of the toys are tagged, you must add.

STEP 3 > **Solve the problem.**
When adding or subtracting fractions with like denominators, add the numerators. Keep the denominators the same. Reduce your answer if possible.
$\frac{3}{8} + \frac{1}{8} = \frac{4}{8} = \frac{1}{2}$ $\frac{1}{2}$ of all the toys are tagged.

Now it's your turn! Choose an operation to solve each problem.

1. Edwin went to the big toy sale. He noticed that $\frac{5}{6}$ of the dinosaur toys were on sale, but only $\frac{4}{6}$ of the shark toys were on sale. What fraction more of the dinosaur toys were on sale?

   _____

2. Edwin decided to buy some party favors. Of his total purchase, $\frac{1}{7}$ were whistles, $\frac{2}{7}$ were tops, and the rest were yo-yos. What fraction of his purchase were yo-yos?

   _____

3. Nora went to the sale, too. She noticed that $\frac{5}{12}$ of the dolls were blonde, and $\frac{3}{12}$ of the dolls were brunette. What fraction of the dolls were blonde or brunette?

   _____

4. What fraction of the dolls were not blonde or brunette?

   _____

5. Gustavo likes action figures. He bought some at the sale. Now in his collection, $\frac{3}{9}$ are hero figures and $\frac{2}{9}$ are aliens. The rest are monsters. What fraction of his collection are monsters?

   _____

Name _____ Date _____

READY, SET, GO!

Sometimes you must work with fractions that do not have like denominators.
Then you must change them into equivalent fractions by reducing them
or changing them to higher terms.

 Read the problem.

One day the gym teacher held a contest. She wanted
to see who could climb higher up a rope. The first
2 climbers were Max and Casey. Max
climbed $\frac{3}{4}$ of the way up the rope. Casey climbed
$\frac{5}{8}$ of the way. Who won the contest?

 Change the fractions to equivalent fractions.

Compare the denominators. 8 is a multiple of 4. So $\frac{3}{4}$ can be
changed to $\frac{6}{8}$ by multiplying the numerator and the denominator by 2.

 Solve the problem.

Compare the 2 fractions.

$\frac{3}{4} = \frac{6}{8}$ $\frac{6}{8}$ is greater than $\frac{5}{8}$. So Max won the contest.

Now it's your turn! Change the fractions into equivalent fractions to solve these problems.

1. Tyler, Megan, and Janna were also in
the rope-climbing contest. Tyler
climbed $\frac{7}{12}$ of the way up the rope,
Megan climbed $\frac{5}{6}$ of the way, and
Janna climbed $\frac{2}{3}$ of the way. Who won
this time?

   _____

2. Another part of the contest was the
running race. Jimmy ran $\frac{4}{5}$ of a mile,
Jarrett ran $\frac{13}{20}$ of a mile, and
Jennifer ran $\frac{7}{10}$ of a mile. Who ran
the farthest?

   _____

3. There was also a free-throw contest.
Each person had 24 shots. Val hit $\frac{7}{8}$ of
his shots, Mary hit $\frac{11}{12}$ of her shots,
and Bobby hit $\frac{3}{4}$ of his shots. Who
won the free-throw contest?

   _____

4. In the last contest, students stood on
their heads as long as they could.
Katie stood on her head for $\frac{1}{2}$ a
minute, Carl stood on his for $\frac{7}{15}$ of a
minute, and Charlene stood on her
head for $\frac{3}{10}$ of a minute. Who won
this contest?

   _____

Name _____ Date _____

WRAP IT UP!

Sometimes a problem will not tell you to add or subtract. Then you must decide which operation to use to solve the problem.

 Read the problem.

Fractions Department Store wraps gifts for customers. On 1 gift Angie used $\frac{3}{5}$ of a roll of ribbon. On another gift she used $\frac{6}{25}$ of a roll of ribbon. What fraction of the roll of ribbon did she use altogether?

 Choose an operation.

To find the total amount of ribbon used, add.

 Solve the problem.

First you must change the fractions into equivalent fractions. Then add. Reduce the answer if possible.

$\frac{3}{5} + \frac{6}{25} = \frac{15}{25} + \frac{6}{25} = \frac{21}{25}$

Angie used $\frac{21}{25}$ of the roll of ribbon.

Now it's your turn! Choose an operation to solve each problem. Reduce your answers if possible.

1. Angie sorted the gift box tops and bottoms. She found $\frac{9}{16}$ of the tops and $\frac{5}{8}$ of the bottoms. Did she find more tops or bottoms?

   _____

2. One day Angie wrapped a big box. She used $\frac{2}{3}$ of a roll of paper to wrap the sides and $\frac{2}{9}$ to wrap the rest of the box. What fraction of a roll of paper did Angie use to wrap the box?

   _____

3. What fraction of the roll of paper was left?

   _____

4. On Thursday Angie used $\frac{1}{8}$ of all the bows to wrap gifts. On Friday she used $\frac{1}{2}$ of all the bows. What fraction of all the bows did Angie use?

   _____

5. What fraction of all the bows were left?

   _____

6. Angie used silver ribbon on $\frac{4}{7}$ of all the gifts she wrapped. She used gold ribbon on all the rest. What fraction of the gifts had gold ribbon?

   _____

A BED FOR FIDO

Sometimes to solve a problem you must use more than 1 operation. You must decide which operations to use and in what order they must be used.

STEP 1 ▷ **Read the problem.**

Camela is going to build a bed for Fido. She needs $\frac{3}{4}$ of a sheet of plywood to build the bed. She found 1 piece that was $\frac{3}{12}$ of a sheet and another that was $\frac{3}{9}$ of a sheet. Does she have enough plywood with these 2 pieces?

STEP 2 ▷ **Make a plan.**

To find how much plywood Camela has, add. To find if she has enough plywood, compare what she has to what she needs.

STEP 3 ▷ **Solve the problem.**

Remember to change the fractions into equivalent fractions.

$\frac{3}{12} + \frac{3}{9} = \frac{9}{36} + \frac{12}{36} = \frac{21}{36} = \frac{7}{12}$ wood she has

Then compare the fractions to see if she has enough.

$\frac{3}{4}$ wood she needs $= \frac{9}{12}$ $\frac{7}{12}$ wood she has

Camela does not have enough wood to build Fido's bed.

Now it's your turn! Make a plan and choose operations to solve each problem.

1. If Camela has $\frac{7}{12}$ of a sheet of plywood and she needs $\frac{3}{4}$ of a sheet to build Fido's bed, how much more plywood does she need?

   _____

2. Camela decides to make a pair of pajamas for poor Fido. She needs $\frac{7}{8}$ of a yard of fabric. She has 1 piece that is $\frac{1}{3}$ of a yard, another piece that is $\frac{1}{4}$ of a yard, and a third piece that is $\frac{5}{12}$ of a yard. Does she have enough fabric to make Fido's pajamas?

   _____

3. On Monday Fido ate $\frac{3}{4}$ of a bag of food. On Tuesday he ate $\frac{1}{6}$ of a bag. What fraction of the bag of food did Fido eat on the 2 days?

   _____

4. What fraction of the bag of food does Fido have left?

   _____

WOODSHOP WORK

Name _____ Date _____

Sometimes to solve a problem you must use more than 1 operation. You must decide which operations to use and in what order they must be used.

STEP 1 ▷ **Read the problem.**

Fran is building display counters. She will use 110 feet of wood to make 5 counters. With 30 feet of wood, she has made a 10-foot counter. With 24 feet of wood she has made an 8-foot counter, and 16 feet of wood made a 4-foot counter. To use all the 110 feet of wood, what are the sizes of the last 2 counters?

STEP 2 ▷ **Identify the facts.**

Fact 1: *Fran will use 110 feet of wood.*

Fact 2: *30 feet or $\frac{30}{110}$ of the wood made a 10-foot counter.*

Fact 3: *24 feet or $\frac{24}{110}$ of the wood made an 8-foot counter.*

Fact 4: *16 feet or $\frac{16}{110}$ of the wood made a 4-foot counter.*

Fact 5: *Fran will make 5 counters.*

STEP 3 ▷ **Make a plan.**

1. To find how much wood has already been used, add.
2. To find how much more wood she has, subtract.
3. To find the sizes of the last 2 counters, use guess and check.

STEP 4 ▷ **Solve the problem.**

1. $\frac{30}{110} + \frac{24}{110} + \frac{16}{110} = \frac{70}{110}$

2. $\frac{110}{110} - \frac{70}{110} = \frac{40}{110}$

   She has 40 feet of wood, or $\frac{40}{110}$, left to make 2 counters.

3. $\frac{40}{110} = \frac{24}{110} + \frac{16}{110}$

   The last 2 sizes will be an 8-foot counter and a 4-foot counter.

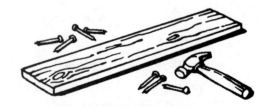

Name _____   Date _____

WOODSHOP WORK, PART 2

30 feet of wood	=	10-foot counter
24 feet of wood	=	8-foot counter
16 feet of wood	=	4-foot counter

Now it's your turn! Use the table and make a plan to solve the problems.

1. Fran made another display. She used a total of 132 feet of wood. She made a 10-foot counter, an 8-foot counter, and 2 of the 4-foot counters. She had to make 2 more counters in different sizes. How many feet of wood did she use for the last 2 counters?

   _____

2. What size counters could she make?

   _____

3. Chuck also make a display. He made 3 of the 10-foot counters, 2 of the 8-foot counters, and a 4-foot counter. How many total feet of counters did he build?

   _____

4. What fraction of the total were the 10-foot counters?

   _____

5. What fraction of the total were the 8-foot counters?

   _____

6. What fraction of the total was the 4-foot counter?

   _____

7. Chuck had 64 feet of wood left over from his earlier project. He had to make at least 2 different sizes of counters. What sizes and how many of each could he make with the leftover wood?

   _____

8. What fraction of the total amount of wood would each size be?

   _____

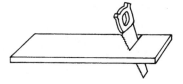

MATH MADNESS

Harriet loves to have fun in her spare time. Solve these problems about Harriet's fun activities.

1 If Harriet eats all but $\frac{1}{4}$ of a pie, how much pie does she have left?

_____

2 Harriet has a really big watermelon. She gives $\frac{1}{2}$ to Jim and $\frac{1}{2}$ to Jane. How much watermelon does she have left for herself?

_____

3 Harriet won $20,000 in a contest. She decided to keep $\frac{1}{2}$ for herself. She gave $\frac{3}{10}$ to her brother and $\frac{1}{5}$ to her sister. How much money did each person get?

_____

4 Using the money she won, Harriet took her wood-working club of 24 people to the fun park. There $\frac{3}{8}$ of the people rode the roller coaster, $\frac{1}{4}$ rode the bumper cars, and $\frac{5}{24}$ rode the water ride. Only $\frac{1}{6}$ went to the funhouse. Did all of the people in Harriet's club do an activity?

_____

5 Harriet needs $\frac{10}{12}$ of a yard of fabric to sew a shirt. She can buy $\frac{5}{6}$ of a yard of fabric for $4.50 or $\frac{3}{4}$ of a yard of fabric for $4.00. Which fabric should she buy to make her shirt?

_____

Name _____ Date _____

LOST IN SPACE!

A proper fraction is one whose numerator is smaller than its denominator. Examples of proper fractions are $\frac{1}{2}$ or $\frac{3}{4}$. Equivalent fractions are fractions that have the same value, though they have different numerators and denominators. For example, $\frac{1}{3}$ and $\frac{2}{6}$ are equivalent fractions. A drawing can often help you to solve problems about fractions more easily.

STEP 1 **Read the problem.**

Thom and Dara were on a secret space mission. But their spaceship was knocked off course by an asteroid. Dara feared they were out of radio range.

One radio signal went $\frac{1}{2}$ of the way back to the base. A second signal went $\frac{2}{4}$ of the way, and a third signal went $\frac{3}{6}$ of the way. Prove that $\frac{1}{2}$ is equivalent to $\frac{2}{4}$ and $\frac{3}{6}$ by shading in these drawings.

STEP 2 **Make a drawing.**

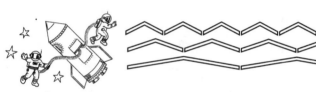

 ### Now it's your turn! Make a drawing to help you solve each problem.

1. When the asteroid hit the spaceship, it damaged the antennas. After the collision, $\frac{3}{4}$ of the radio antenna was left, and $\frac{9}{12}$ of the telescope antenna remained. Which antenna had more remaining?

   _____

2. Thom and Dara were lost in space. On Monday they used $\frac{3}{10}$ tank of fuel. On Tuesday they used $\frac{2}{5}$ tank of fuel. On which day did they use more fuel?

   _____

3. Because they were lost, Thom worried $\frac{1}{3}$ of the time and Dara worried $\frac{3}{9}$ of the time. Who worried more?

   _____

4. On Wednesday Dara spent $\frac{3}{10}$ of her time sending radio signals. Thom spent $\frac{3}{5}$ of his time sending signals. Who spent more time sending radio signals?

   _____

WILL WE SURVIVE?

Sometimes solving a problem means using more than 1 operation.

An improper fraction is one whose numerator is greater than or equal to its denominator. Both $\frac{6}{6}$ and $\frac{7}{6}$ are improper fractions. To change improper fractions into mixed numbers, first divide the numerator by the denominator. If there is a remainder, write the remainder over the denominator.

$\frac{6}{6}$ (improper fraction) = 6 ÷ 6 = 1 (whole number)

$\frac{7}{6}$ (improper fraction) = 7 ÷ 6 = 1 R1 = $1\frac{1}{6}$ (mixed number)

Read the problem.

 On Thursday Dara checked their food supply. One storage locker held $\frac{32}{10}$ pounds of food. Another locker held $\frac{28}{10}$ pounds, and a third held $\frac{40}{10}$ pounds. If they share the food equally, how many pounds do Thom and Dara each have left?

Make a plan.

 Add the amounts of food in the 3 storage lockers. Change the improper fractions into mixed or whole numbers. Divide the total amount of food remaining by 2.

Use the plan to solve the problem.

 Reduce answers if possible.

$\frac{32}{10} + \frac{28}{10} + \frac{40}{10} = \frac{100}{10}$ pounds of food remaining

$\frac{100}{10} = 10$ pounds ÷ 2 = 5 pounds

Thom and Dara each have 5 pounds of food left.

Now it's your turn! Make a plan to solve each problem.

1. Thom checked the oxygen supply. One canister held $\frac{9}{5}$ units, a second held $\frac{13}{5}$ units, and a third held $\frac{6}{5}$ units. If together Thom and Dara used $\frac{10}{5}$ units of oxygen a day, did they have enough oxygen for 3 days?

   _____

2. If they began with $\frac{200}{5}$ units, how much oxygen had they used?

   _____

3. Thom also checked the fuel supply. One tank held $\frac{8}{4}$ liters, another held $\frac{14}{4}$ liters, and a third held $\frac{11}{4}$ liters. How much fuel did they have left?

   _____

4. If they began with $\frac{100}{4}$ liters, how much fuel had they used?

   _____

Name _____ Date _____

WHERE ARE WE?

To add or subtract fractions, it is often easier to have fractions with like denominators. So you might need to change one or more of the fractions into equivalent fractions. To reduce, or simplify, a fraction you must find the smallest equivalent fraction. To find the smallest equivalent, divide the numerator and denominator by the greatest possible number. To change the fraction to an equivalent fraction in higher terms, multiply the numerator and denominator by the same number. Writing a number sentence can help you to solve a problem more easily.

 STEP 1 **Read the problem.**

On the first day after the collision, the spaceship traveled $\frac{3}{4}$ light-year. On the second day it traveled $\frac{2}{3}$ light-year. How far did the spaceship travel on the 2 days?

STEP 2 **Write a number sentence.**

$\frac{3}{4}$ light-year + $\frac{2}{3}$ light-year = total distance traveled

 STEP 3 **Solve the problem.**

Since $\frac{3}{4}$ and $\frac{2}{3}$ cannot be reduced, you must change them into equivalent fractions in higher terms. Reduce your answer if possible.

$\frac{3}{4} = \frac{9}{12}$ $\frac{2}{3} = \frac{8}{12}$ $\frac{9}{12} + \frac{8}{12} = \frac{17}{12} = 1\frac{5}{12}$

The spaceship traveled $1\frac{5}{12}$ light-years on the 2 days.

Now it's your turn! Write a number sentence to help you solve each problem. Reduce your answers if possible.

1. Each day Thom had to write in the ship log. On the first day he wrote $\frac{3}{4}$ page. On the second day he wrote $\frac{7}{8}$ page. On the third day he wrote $\frac{1}{2}$ page. On which day did he write the most?

   _____

2. How many pages did he write altogether?

   _____

3. Dara finally located 2 nearby planets. Planet K was $\frac{2}{3}$ light-year away. Planet Z was $\frac{3}{5}$ light-year away. Which planet was closer?

   _____

4. What was the difference in distance between the 2 planets?

   _____

Name _____ Date _____

PLANET, HO!

Sometimes a problem does not tell you to add or subtract. You must read the problem carefully to choose the correct operation.

 Read the problem.

Dara and Thom decided to go to Planet Z. On the first day they traveled $1\frac{1}{5}$ light-years. On the second day they traveled $1\frac{3}{10}$ light-years. How far did they travel altogether?

 Choose an operation.

To find how far they traveled, add.

 Solve the problem.

To add, you must have fractions with like denominators. First change the fractions into equivalent fractions. $\frac{1}{5} = \frac{2}{10}$. $\frac{3}{10}$ does not need to be changed. Reduce the answer if possible.

$1\frac{2}{10} + 1\frac{3}{10} = 2\frac{5}{10} = 2\frac{1}{2}$

They traveled $2\frac{1}{2}$ light-years altogether.

Now it's your turn! Choose an operation to solve each problem.

1. Dara located 2 landing spots. The first was $9\frac{1}{2}$ space miles away. The second was $9\frac{3}{8}$ space miles away. Which landing spot was closer?

   _____

2. How much closer was the closer landing spot?

   _____

3. After landing, Thom checked their fuel supply again. One fuel tank held $1\frac{3}{4}$ liters, another held $2\frac{2}{3}$ liters, and the third tank was empty. How much fuel did they have left?

   _____

4. Even though Thom and Dara used less oxygen than usual, the oxygen supply was also low. The first tank held $1\frac{1}{5}$ units, and a second tank held $1\frac{7}{10}$ units. Which tank held more oxygen?

   _____

5. How much oxygen did they have left?

   _____

6. If they started with 40 units of oxygen, how much oxygen had they used?

   _____

Name _____ Date _____

LET'S GO EXPLORING!

Often a problem does not tell you to add or subtract to find the answer. You must read the problem carefully to choose the correct operation.

STEP 1 > **Read the problem.**

Thom and Dara decided to explore the planet. On the first day they walked $3\frac{1}{2}$ space miles. On the second day they walked $2\frac{4}{5}$ space miles. How far did they walk on the 2 days?

STEP 2 > **Choose an operation.**

To find how far they walked, add.

STEP 3 > **Solve the problem.**

To add the fractions, you must have fractions with like denominators. Change the fractions into equivalent fractions. Reduce your answer if possible.

$3\frac{1}{2} = 3\frac{5}{10}$ $2\frac{4}{5} = 2\frac{8}{10}$

$3\frac{5}{10} + 2\frac{8}{10} = 5\frac{13}{10} = 6\frac{3}{10}$

They walked $6\frac{3}{10}$ miles on the 2 days.

Now it's your turn! Choose an operation to solve each problem.

1. On the first day Thom collected $3\frac{7}{8}$ pounds of rock samples. Dara collected $3\frac{3}{4}$ pounds of rock samples. Who collected more rock samples?

   _____

2. How much more?

   _____

3. On the third day Thom and Dara walked for $2\frac{1}{2}$ hours. On the fourth day they walked for $4\frac{9}{10}$ hours. How many hours did they walk on the 2 days?

   _____

4. How much longer did they walk on the fourth day than on the third day?

   _____

5. On the third day Thom ate $\frac{7}{16}$ pound of food. Dara ate $\frac{3}{8}$ pound of food. How much food did they eat together?

   _____

BACK TO EARTH!

Using common sense is a logical way to solve a problem. Logic will help you to decide if the answer to a problem seems reasonable.

On the fifth day Thom and Dara found a magic maze. A sign by the entrance said that the maze was really a time warp. Anyone who could find all the magic numbers would magically arrive back on Earth.

Now it's your turn!

Help Thom and Dara get back to Earth. At each gate in the maze, match the gate letter to the problem with that letter. Then solve each problem either by reducing the fractions or changing them into equivalent fractions with higher terms. Reduce your answers if possible. If the answer matches a magic number, that gate will open. Thom and Dara will move closer back to Earth. If the answer does not match a magic number, Thom and Dara must change directions in the maze.

Here are the magic numbers:
$3\frac{7}{13}$, $\frac{1}{4}$, $1\frac{1}{2}$, $\frac{9}{16}$, $1\frac{1}{3}$, $10\frac{7}{12}$, $4\frac{3}{16}$, $1\frac{11}{24}$.

Hint: You can solve all the problems to find which answers are magic numbers. Or you can use logic to choose a path for Thom and Dara and only try to open the gates on the path you've chosen. Good luck!

Here are the problems to solve:

A. $\frac{5}{8} - \frac{1}{8} =$ _____

B. $\frac{1}{2} - \frac{1}{12} =$ _____

C. $4\frac{9}{13} - 1\frac{2}{13} =$ _____

D. $3\frac{2}{3} + 5\frac{8}{9} =$ _____

E. $\frac{7}{16} - \frac{3}{16} =$ _____

F. $\frac{4}{5} + \frac{7}{10} =$ _____

G. $\frac{5}{16} + \frac{1}{4} =$ _____

H. $7\frac{1}{6} + 2\frac{5}{6} =$ _____

I. $\frac{15}{16} - \frac{3}{16} =$ _____

J. $2\frac{3}{4} - \frac{2}{8} =$ _____

K. $\frac{3}{5} - \frac{1}{2} =$ _____

L. $5\frac{11}{14} + 9\frac{11}{28} =$ _____

M. $\frac{1}{2} + \frac{3}{8} =$ _____

N. $\frac{8}{9} + \frac{4}{9} =$ _____

O. $\frac{4}{9} + \frac{1}{3} =$ _____

P. $\frac{9}{3} - \frac{6}{3} =$ _____

Q. $8\frac{1}{4} - 6\frac{1}{5} =$ _____

R. $1\frac{1}{2} + 9\frac{1}{12} =$ _____

S. $\frac{18}{4} - \frac{5}{16} =$ _____

T. $\frac{7}{4} + \frac{11}{6} =$ _____

Name _____ Date _____

BACK TO EARTH! PART 2

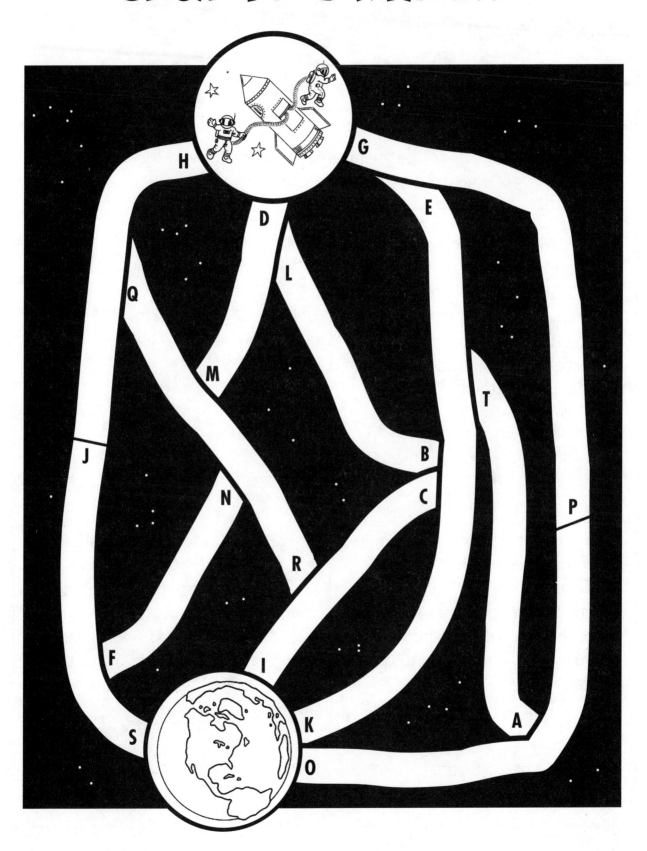

Name _____ Date _____

MATH MADNESS

One day Harriet decided to organize her house and workshop. Help Harriet get organized by solving these problems.

1 Harriet found some boxes of books in a closet. She had 2 boxes of adventure stories, $\frac{2}{5}$ of a box of mysteries, and $\frac{1}{5}$ of a box of comic books. How many boxes of books did she have altogether?

_____

3 Harriet also found some old paint in her workshop. She had $1\frac{1}{2}$ cans of red paint, $2\frac{3}{4}$ cans of white paint, and $\frac{2}{3}$ can of black paint. How many cans of paint did she have altogether?

_____

2 Harriet decided to arrange her music collection. She had 100 CDs. Of these, $\frac{1}{4}$ were country music, $\frac{2}{5}$ were rock music, and $\frac{7}{20}$ were hip-hop music. How many CDs of each kind did Harriet have?

_____

4 Harriet found some short pieces of board in her workshop, too. One piece was $\frac{3}{4}$ foot long, a second was $2\frac{1}{3}$ foot long, a third was $1\frac{5}{6}$ foot long, and a fourth was $3\frac{1}{2}$ feet long. Altogether, how many feet of board did Harriet find?

_____

Name _____ Date _____

SPORTS FRACTIONS

When you are working with fractions, you may not know whether to add, subtract, multiply, or divide. HINT: Sometimes a problem will ask you something like, "How much is $\frac{2}{3}$ of 3?" The word *of* is the signal to multiply.

 Read the problem.

Beto was at the driving range. He had 40 golf balls. He hit $\frac{3}{4}$ of the balls. How many balls did Beto hit?

 Identify the facts.

Beto had 40 golf balls. He hit $\frac{3}{4}$ of the balls.

 Choose an operation.

The word *of* in the question means multiply.

 Solve the problem.

When you multiply fractions and whole numbers, you must first change the whole number to a fraction. $40 = \frac{40}{1}$

Then multiply the numerators. Then multiply the denominators. $\frac{3}{4} \times \frac{40}{1} = \frac{120}{4}$

Then reduce the fraction. $\frac{120}{4} = \frac{30}{1} = 30$

Beto hit 30 golf balls.

Now it's your turn! Solve the following problems. Reduce the answers if possible.

1. Alice was shooting arrows at a target. She had 12 arrows to shoot, and $\frac{1}{3}$ of her arrows hit near the bullseye. How many arrows hit near the bullseye?

   _____

2. Derek was shooting free throws. He shot 48 times. He made $\frac{2}{3}$ of his shots. How many free throws did Derek make?

   _____

3. Suzy was the pitcher for the softball team. In one game she threw 100 pitches, and $\frac{3}{5}$ of Suzy's pitches were strikes. How many of Suzy's pitches were strikes?

   _____

4. How many of Suzy's pitches were balls?

   _____

Name _____ Date _____

MAIL CALL

Sometimes solving a problem means using more than 1 operation. Decide whether to add, subtract, multiply, or divide, and then decide how to combine these operations.

 Read the problem.

Hoang sorts and delivers the hospital mail. On Monday the hospital received 165 letters. Hoang delivered $\frac{1}{3}$ of these to patients. How many letters did he deliver to patients?

 Choose an operation.

To solve the problem you must find $\frac{1}{3}$ of 165. Remember the signal word *of*. Multiply.

 Solve the problem.

$$\frac{1}{3} \times \frac{165}{1} = \frac{1 \times 165}{3 \times 1} = \frac{165}{3} = 55$$

Hoang delivered 55 letters to patients.

Now it's your turn! Choose 1 or more operations. Multiply the fractions to solve the problems.

1. On Monday there were 165 letters. The patients received $\frac{1}{3}$ of the mail and the doctors received $\frac{2}{5}$ of the mail. What fraction of the mail did the other departments receive?

   _____

2. How many letters did the other departments receive?

   _____

3. On Monday $\frac{2}{5}$ of 165 letters were for the doctors. On Tuesday $\frac{1}{4}$ of 124 letters were for the doctors. How many letters did the doctors receive on the 2 days?

   _____

4. The church group donated $\frac{7}{8}$ of their 80 magazines to the hospital. Ms. Bell used $\frac{3}{5}$ of the donated magazines for scrapbooks for the children. How many magazines were donated?

   _____

5. How many magazines were used for scrapbooks?

   _____

Unit IV: Multiplying Fractions

© Steck-Vaughn Company

40

Problem Solving 5-6, SV 6761-1

AT THE HOSPITAL

Number sentences help to show how numbers relate to each other.

STEP 1 **Read the problem.**

Al has a job after school at the hospital washroom. To wash the sheets Al uses $\frac{1}{4}$ cup bleach in every load. He uses $\frac{2}{3}$ as much fabric softener as bleach. How much fabric softener does he use for each load?

STEP 2 **Identify the facts.**

Al uses $\frac{1}{4}$ cup bleach in every load. He uses $\frac{2}{3}$ as much fabric softener as bleach.

STEP 3 **Write a number sentence.**

$\frac{1}{4}$ cup bleach $\times$ $\frac{2}{3}$ as much softener = total amount of softener

STEP 4 **Solve the problem.**

Reduce the answer if possible.

$$\frac{1}{4} \times \frac{2}{3} = \frac{1 \times 2}{4 \times 3} = \frac{2}{12} = \frac{1}{6}$$

Al uses $\frac{1}{6}$ cup of fabric softener.

Now it's your turn! Write number sentences to help you solve the problems. Reduce your answers if possible.

1. Al uses $\frac{7}{8}$ cup of soap to wash the lab coats. He uses $\frac{1}{2}$ as much bleach as soap. How much bleach does he use for a load of lab coats?

   _____

2. The hospital cook made soup on Saturday. She added $\frac{3}{4}$ cup of salt and $\frac{1}{3}$ as much pepper as salt. How much pepper did she use?

   _____

3. For vegetable soup, the cook used $\frac{2}{5}$ as much broth as water. She used 15 cups of water. How much broth did she use?

   _____

4. The hospital was staffed by 78 people on Saturday. $\frac{5}{6}$ of the staff ate lunch in the cafeteria. Of these people, $\frac{3}{5}$ work in the washroom. How many of the staff who ate lunch in the cafeteria work in the washroom?

   _____

Name _____   Date _____

VROOM!

One way to solve problems is to guess the answer, then check it. If it is not right, try again. Use what you learn from the first guess to make your next guess better. Guess and check until you find the right answer.

 Read the problem.
Carri liked to drive miniature race cars. One day her car started with $2\frac{1}{3}$ gallons of gas. She used $\frac{1}{2}$ of the gas. How many gallons of gas did she use?

 Identify the facts.
Fact 1: Carri started with $2\frac{1}{3}$ gallons of gas.
Fact 2: She used $\frac{1}{2}$ of the gas.

Guess the answer.
First you can multiply the fraction by the whole number.
$\frac{1}{2}$ of $2 = \frac{1}{2} \times \frac{2}{1} = \frac{2}{2} = 1$
Then multiply the fractions.
$\frac{1}{2} \times \frac{1}{3} = \frac{1}{6}$
Then add the two numbers. $1 + \frac{1}{6} = 1\frac{1}{6}$ gallons

Check your answer.
When multiplying a fraction by a mixed number, you can change the mixed number to a fraction.
$2\frac{1}{3} = \frac{7}{3}$
Then multiply. $\frac{7}{3} \times \frac{1}{2} = \frac{7}{6}$
Then reduce. $\frac{7}{6} = 1\frac{1}{6}$. Your answer is correct.

Now it's your turn! Use guessing and checking to solve these problems.

1. The race track was $1\frac{3}{4}$ miles long. Carri drove $\frac{4}{5}$ of the way before her car broke down. How many miles did Carri drive?

   _____

2. Once Carri was able to drive $6\frac{1}{2}$ laps before she ran out of gas. Today she only went $\frac{2}{3}$ that far before she ran out of gas. How many laps did Carri drive today before she ran out of gas?

   _____

Name _____ Date _____

WHO WANTS PIZZA?

Sometimes using a graph can help you to solve a problem more easily.

STEP 1 **Read the problem.**

Emily and Anton work at the pizza parlor. Every day they use $20\frac{1}{2}$ pounds of flour to make pizzas. They use $\frac{1}{4}$ of that flour to make pepperoni pizzas. They use $\frac{1}{8}$ of the flour to make olive pizzas. Is more flour used to make pepperoni or olive pizzas?

STEP 2 **Draw a graph to help you organize the facts.**

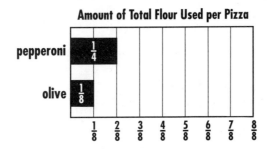

STEP 3 **Use the graph and logic to solve the problem.**

You can see that $\frac{1}{4}$ is more than $\frac{1}{8}$.

STEP 4 **Solve the problem.**

Since $\frac{1}{4}$ of the flour is more than $\frac{1}{8}$ of the flour, more flour is used for pepperoni pizzas than olive pizzas.

Now it's your turn! Use the graph above and logic to help you solve these problems.

1. What fraction of the flour is used to make both the pepperoni and olive pizzas?

   _____

2. What fraction of the flour is used to make other kinds of pizzas?

   _____

3. How many pounds of flour are used to make pepperoni pizzas?

   _____

4. How many pounds of flour are used to make olive pizzas?

   _____

5. How many pounds of flour are used to make the other kinds of pizzas?

   _____

Name _____ Date _____

MAKING TACOS

Writing a number sentence can help you to solve problems more easily.

 Read the problem.

Luis was making tacos. He put $1\frac{1}{3}$ teaspoons of pepper in the taco meat. He added $1\frac{1}{2}$ times as much salt as pepper. How many teaspoons of salt did he use?

 Identify the facts.

Fact 1: Luis used $1\frac{1}{3}$ teaspoons of pepper.
Fact 2: He used $1\frac{1}{2}$ times as much salt as pepper.

 Write a number sentence to solve the problem.

When multiplying a mixed number by a mixed number, change both mixed numbers into improper fractions.

$1\frac{1}{3}$ teaspoons pepper $\times 1\frac{1}{2}$ times more salt $= \frac{4}{3} \times \frac{3}{2}$
Multiply the numerators, and then the denominators.

$\frac{4}{3} \times \frac{3}{2} = \frac{12}{6}$
Reduce the answer.

$\frac{12}{6} = 2$
Luis used 2 teaspoons of salt.

Now it's your turn! Write number sentences to help you solve these problems.

1. Luis also made beans to eat. He used $1\frac{7}{8}$ cups of beans. Then he added $3\frac{1}{3}$ times as much water as beans. How many cups of water did he use?

   _____

2. Luis made a rice dish, too. For spices, he used $1\frac{3}{4}$ teaspoons of cumin. Then he added $1\frac{1}{3}$ times as much garlic salt as cumin. How many teaspoons of garlic salt did he use?

   _____

GLUB, GLUB!

Sometimes a problem requires several steps to solve.

 Read the problem.
Ben could hold his breath underwater for $1\frac{1}{4}$ minutes.
Ashley could hold her breath $1\frac{1}{3}$ times longer than Ben.
How many seconds could Ashley hold her breath?

 Identify the facts.
Fact 1: Ben could hold his breath for $1\frac{1}{4}$ minutes.
Fact 2: Ashley could hold her breath $1\frac{1}{3}$ times longer than Ben.

 Make a plan.
First you must figure how many minutes Ashley could hold her breath. Multiply the two mixed numbers. Then you must figure how many seconds Ashley could hold her breath. Multiply the number of minutes by 60 seconds.

 Solve the problem.
First figure the minutes.
$1\frac{1}{4} \times 1\frac{1}{3} = \frac{5}{4} \times \frac{4}{3} = \frac{20}{12} = 1\frac{8}{12} = 1\frac{3}{4}$
Ashley could hold her breath for $1\frac{3}{4}$ minutes. Now figure the seconds.
$1\frac{3}{4}$ minutes $\times$ 60 seconds per minute $= \frac{7}{4} \times \frac{60}{1} = \frac{420}{4} = 105$
Ashley could hold her breath for 105 seconds.

Now it's your turn! Make a plan, then solve each problem.

1. Cheryl could swim a lap in $1\frac{3}{5}$ minutes. Sid took $1\frac{1}{4}$ times longer than Cheryl. How many seconds faster could Cheryl swim a lap than Sid?

   _____

2. April swam a lap in $2\frac{1}{3}$ minutes using the crawl stroke. When she used the dog paddle, she took $1\frac{1}{2}$ times longer. How many seconds did it take April to swim a lap using the dog paddle?

   _____

3. How many minutes faster could she swim the crawl than the dog paddle?

   _____

Name _____ Date _____

MATH MADNESS

To exercise her brain, Harriet likes to work problems that are short and quick. Help her solve these quickies.

1. How much is $\frac{2}{3}$ of $\frac{3}{4}$? _____

2. How much is $\frac{2}{3}$ of $\frac{3}{4}$ of 8? _____

3. How much is $\frac{2}{3}$ of $\frac{3}{4}$ of 50? _____

Do you see the pattern? Finding a pattern can help you to solve problems more easily.

4. How much is $\frac{1}{2}$ of 96? _____

5. How much is $\frac{1}{2}$ of 48? _____

6. How much is $\frac{1}{2}$ of 24? _____

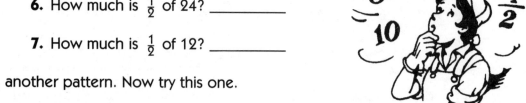

7. How much is $\frac{1}{2}$ of 12? _____

See, another pattern. Now try this one.

8. 90 x _____ = 60

9. 60 x _____ = 40

OK, now see if you can discover what the pattern is here.

10. How much is 2 x 1,234 x $\frac{1}{2}$? _____

11. How much is 4 x 1,234 x $\frac{1}{4}$? _____

12. How much is 3 x 1,234 x $\frac{1}{3}$? _____

Name _____ Date _____

SIGN IN, PLEASE!

Number sentences show how numbers relate to each other. Writing a number sentence can help you to solve a problem more easily.

 Read the problem.

Alpha signed in 8 salespeople at the hospital front desk this week. To find the number of people who might visit in a month, she must divide the number of people who visit in a week by $\frac{1}{4}$. This fraction equals 1 week or $\frac{1}{4}$ of a month. How many salespeople might Alpha sign in this month?

STEP 2 **Write a number sentence.**

8 salespeople $\div \frac{1}{4}$ = salespeople who might sign in this month

STEP 3 **Solve the problem.**

First change the whole number into an improper fraction. $8 = \frac{8}{1}$
To divide by a fraction, invert the second fraction (divisor) to find its reciprocal. The reciprocal of $\frac{1}{4}$ is $\frac{4}{1}$. Then multiply the first fraction by the reciprocal of the second fraction. Reduce your answer if possible.

$$8 \div \frac{1}{4} = \frac{8}{1} \div \frac{4}{1} = \frac{32}{1} = 32$$

32 salespeople might sign in this month.

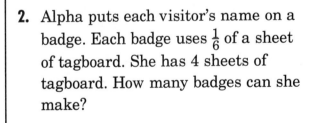

Now it's your turn! Write a number sentence to help you solve each problem.

1. Alpha wants to know how many salespeople might sign in this year. She must divide the number of salespeople who sign in this month by $\frac{1}{12}$. This fraction represents 1 month, or $\frac{1}{12}$ of a year. This month 32 salespeople signed in. How many salespeople can Alpha expect in a year?

   _____

2. Alpha puts each visitor's name on a badge. Each badge uses $\frac{1}{6}$ of a sheet of tagboard. She has 4 sheets of tagboard. How many badges can she make?

   _____

3. A quarter is 25 cents, or $\frac{1}{4}$ of a dollar. How many quarters are in $5.00?

   _____

THINGS TO SHARE

Sometimes you need to work backwards to solve a problem. Write a number sentence to help you.

 Read the problem.

Every week Miriam buys a bouquet of flowers and shares them with 2 other people in her office. This week she divided $\frac{3}{5}$ of the bouquet among all 3 of them, but she kept the rest of the bouquet (all the yellow flowers) for herself. What fraction of the bouquet did Miriam keep for herself?

 Identify the facts.

Fact 1: There are 3 people in the office.

Fact 2: Miriam divided $\frac{3}{5}$ of the bouquet among the 3 of them.

Fact 3: Miriam kept the rest of the bouquet, the yellow flowers, for herself.

 Write a number sentence.

$\frac{3}{5} \div 3$ + yellow flowers = part of bouquet Miriam kept

 Work backwards to solve the problem.

a. Change the whole number into an improper fraction. $3 = \frac{3}{1}$

b. Invert the second fraction (divisor) to find its reciprocal.
   The reciprocal of $\frac{3}{1}$ is $\frac{1}{3}$.

c. To divide by a fraction, multiply the first fraction by the reciprocal of the second fraction. Reduce the answer if possible.

$$\frac{3}{5} \div 3 = \frac{3}{5} \div \frac{3}{1} = \frac{3}{5} \times \frac{1}{3} = \frac{3}{15} = \frac{1}{5}$$

   Each person shared $\frac{1}{5}$ of the bouquet.

d. To find the fraction of the bouquet that were yellow flowers, subtract the fraction from the whole.

$$1 - \frac{3}{5} = \frac{5}{5} - \frac{3}{5} = \frac{2}{5}$$

   The yellow flowers were $\frac{2}{5}$ of the bouquet.

e. To find the fraction of the bouquet that Miriam kept, add her part of the shared fraction of the bouquet to the yellow flowers.
   $\frac{1}{5}$ (Miriam's share) + $\frac{2}{5}$ (yellow flowers) = $\frac{3}{5}$
   Miriam kept $\frac{3}{5}$ of the whole bouquet for herself.

THINGS TO SHARE, PART 2

Now it's your turn! Write a number sentence for each problem to show how the numbers are related to each other. Then work backwards to solve each problem. Reduce your answers if possible.

1. Miriam, Claudia, and Francisco work in the hospital's medical records office. On Friday afternoon they still had to finish checking $\frac{2}{3}$ of the patient files. They divided the files evenly so they could finish the work. What fraction of the remaining files did each person check?

_____

2. On Tuesday Claudia brought in $\frac{3}{4}$ of a dozen donuts. She shared them equally with Miriam and Francisco. What fraction of the dozen donuts did each person get?

_____

3. How many donuts did each person get?

_____

4. On Thursday Francisco brought in $\frac{1}{2}$ of a gallon of juice. Miriam, Claudia, and he each drank an equal amount of the juice. What fraction of the juice did each person drink?

_____

5. On Friday Miriam's friend Bob brought in $\frac{5}{6}$ of a box of candy. He shared it equally with Miriam, Claudia, and Francisco. What fraction of the candy did each person get?

_____

6. If the whole box of candy had 24 pieces, how many pieces of candy did each person get?

_____

CHEERFUL CANDY STRIPERS

Sometimes a drawing helps to organize the information in a problem. Be sure to include all the important facts in a drawing.

  Read the problem.

Three candy stripers visited the hospital's elderly patients. They divided their time evenly so each would have a turn. Altogether, they worked for a total of $5\frac{2}{5}$ hours. How much time did each candy striper spend with elderly patients?

  Identify the facts.

There were 3 candy stripers. They divided their time evenly. They worked a total of $5\frac{2}{5}$ hours.

  Make a drawing.

Each box is divided into fifths. Each box represents 1 hour.

STEP 4 **Solve the problem.**

Divide the boxes into 3 equal groups. Circle each group.

Altogether, there are 27 fifths, or $\frac{27}{5}$.

There are 3 groups. So each group contains $\frac{9}{5}$. $\frac{9}{5} = 1\frac{4}{5}$

Each candy striper worked $1\frac{4}{5}$ hours.

Now it's your turn! Make a drawing to help you solve each problem.

1. For a snack, the 3 candy stripers ate $3\frac{3}{4}$ ounces of carrots. If they shared the carrots equally, how many ounces of carrots did each candy striper eat?

   _____

2. The 3 candy stripers pooled their money and bought $7\frac{1}{3}$ dozen flowers from the gift shop. If they divided the flowers equally among 4 patients, how many dozen flowers did each patient get?

   _____

3. How many flowers did each patient get?

   _____

4. If the candy stripers used $4\frac{4}{5}$ sheets of paper to write notes about 6 patients, how many sheets did they use for each patient?

   _____

Name _____   Date _____

A MULTICULTURAL FEAST

Some problems give too many facts. If there are too many facts, cross out the extra facts. Then work the problem.

STEP 1 **Read the problem.**

Sharona worked in the hospital. She asked everyone to bring something for the multicultural party. She brought $6\frac{2}{3}$ packages of rice cakes and $4\frac{7}{8}$ pounds of tofu. If she divided the packages of rice cakes by $\frac{1}{3}$ to make more packages, how many smaller packages of rice cakes would she have?

STEP 2 **Identify the facts you need and don't need.**

Need: Sharona brought $6\frac{2}{3}$ packages of rice cakes.
Need: She divided the packages of rice cakes by $\frac{1}{3}$.
Don't need: She brought $4\frac{7}{8}$ pounds of tofu.

STEP 3 **Solve the problem.**

Change the mixed number into an improper fraction: $6\frac{2}{3} = \frac{20}{3}$. Invert the second fraction (divisor) to find the reciprocal: $\frac{1}{3}$ becomes $\frac{3}{1}$. To divide, multiply the improper fraction by the reciprocal. Reduce the answer. $\frac{20}{3} \times \frac{3}{1} = \frac{60}{3} = 20$
She would have 20 smaller packages of rice cakes.

Now it's your turn! Cross out the extra facts. Then solve the problems.

1. Mr. Olson brought Swedish meatballs to the party. He bought 2 pounds of beef. His recipe makes $9\frac{1}{2}$ large meatballs. If he divides the number of meatballs by $\frac{1}{4}$, he will have enough smaller meatballs for everyone. How many smaller meatballs can he make?

    _____

2. Simone made Greek baklava for the party. She used $\frac{1}{2}$ cup of nuts and $\frac{3}{4}$ cup of honey in the recipe. She cut 10 pieces from 1 pan. If she divided the pieces by $\frac{1}{3}$, how many slices would she have?

    _____

Name _____ Date _____

EVERYDAY HOSPITAL TASKS

Some problems do not tell you to add, subtract, multiply, or divide. Read the problem carefully to help you to choose the correct operation.

 Read the problem.

Pat has $15\frac{2}{5}$ yards of gauze to make bandages. Each bandage uses $1\frac{2}{5}$ yards. How many bandages can Pat make?

 Identify the facts.

Pat has $15\frac{2}{5}$ yards of gauze. Each bandage uses $1\frac{2}{5}$ yards of gauze.

 Choose an operation.

Divide $15\frac{2}{5}$ by $1\frac{2}{5}$ to find the number of bandages Pat can make.

 Solve the problem.

$15\frac{2}{5} \div 1\frac{2}{5} = \frac{77}{5} \div \frac{7}{5} = \frac{77}{5} \times \frac{5}{7} = \frac{385}{35} = 11$

Pat can make 11 bandages.

Now it's your turn! Choose an operation to solve each problem.

1. Pat has $56\frac{1}{4}$ pounds of plaster. If 1 cast uses $3\frac{3}{4}$ pounds of plaster, how many casts can Pat make?

   _____

2. Pat can wrap a bandage with $1\frac{1}{10}$ yards of tape. If he has $8\frac{4}{5}$ yards of tape, how many bandages can he wrap?

   _____

3. The nursery uses $2\frac{1}{4}$ packages of cotton balls every day. There are $13\frac{1}{2}$ packages on the shelf. How many days' supply of cotton balls does the nursery have?

   _____

4. The emergency room uses $9\frac{3}{4}$ times more cotton balls in a month than the nursery uses in a day. If the nursery uses $2\frac{2}{3}$ packages in a day, how many packages does the emergency room use in a month?

   _____

FUN WITH THE CANDY STRIPERS!

Some problems can be solved by recognizing a pattern. Look for a pattern.
Use the pattern to help you solve the problem more easily.

STEP 1 > Read the problem.

What are the missing numbers in this pattern?

dividend		divisor						quotient		reduced quotient
$\frac{3}{4}$	$\div$	$\frac{1}{2}$	$=$	$\frac{3}{4}$	$\times$	$\frac{2}{1}$	$=$	$\frac{6}{4}$	$=$	$1\frac{1}{2}$
$\frac{3}{4}$	$\div$	$\frac{1}{4}$	$=$	$\frac{3}{4}$	$\times$	$\frac{4}{1}$	$=$	$\frac{12}{4}$	$=$	3
$\frac{3}{4}$	$\div$	$\frac{1}{8}$	$=$	$\frac{3}{4}$	$\times$	$\frac{8}{1}$	$=$	$\frac{24}{4}$	$=$	6
$\frac{3}{4}$	$\div$	___	$=$	$\frac{3}{4}$	$\times$	___	$=$	___	$=$	___

STEP 2 > Find the pattern.

Determine the relationship of the numbers. Each divisor is $\frac{1}{2}$ smaller than the previous divisor. Each quotient is twice as much as the previous quotient.

STEP 3 > Write the rule for the pattern.

Multiply each divisor by $\frac{1}{2}$.

STEP 4 > Solve the problem.

Fill in the missing numbers in the table.

Now it's your turn! Find a pattern. Use the pattern to help you solve the problem.

1. The candy stripers held a contest. The children had to roll a ball down the hall. To award points, they divided the length of the roll by $\frac{1}{5}$. How many points did each child score? Fill in the blanks in the table.

child	dividend		divisor					quotient		points scored
Ruben	$\frac{5}{6}$	$\div$	$\frac{1}{5}$	$=$	$\frac{5}{6}$	$\times$	$\frac{5}{1}$	$=$	$\frac{25}{6}$	$=$	$4\frac{1}{6}$
Milly	$\frac{4}{6}$	$\div$	$\frac{1}{5}$	$=$	$\frac{4}{6}$	$\times$	$\frac{5}{1}$	$=$	___	$=$	___
Chan	$\frac{}{6}$	$\div$	$\frac{1}{5}$	$=$	$\frac{}{6}$	$\times$	$\frac{5}{1}$	$=$	___	$=$	___
Rosa	$\frac{2}{6}$	$\div$	$\frac{1}{5}$	$=$	$\frac{2}{6}$	$\times$	$\frac{5}{1}$	$=$	___	$=$	___
Skip	$\frac{}{6}$	$\div$	$\frac{1}{5}$	$=$	$\frac{}{6}$	$\times$	$\frac{5}{1}$	$=$	___	$=$	___

Name _____ Date _____

MATH MADNESS

One evening Harriet was sitting by her backyard pond. She was thinking about all the math she had learned recently. Help Harriet review by solving these problems.

1 In her job as a delivery driver, Harriet had worked a total of 97.5 hours. She had earned $5.70 an hour. How much were her total earnings from her delivery job?

_____

2 Harriet's garden had done well. She had harvested $7\frac{1}{4}$ pounds of squash and $8\frac{2}{3}$ pounds of beans. How many total pounds of these vegetables did she harvest?

_____

3 Harriet's tomatoes also did well. She harvested $10\frac{1}{2}$ pounds of tomatoes. She gave $\frac{1}{3}$ of these to her neighbors. How many pounds of tomatoes did she give to her neighbors?

_____

4 Harriet admired the flowers in her garden. She had 12 yellow flowers and 9 red flowers. What was the ratio of red flowers to yellow flowers?

_____

5 Harriet was planning to build a square shed in her backyard. If the floor size was 8 feet by 8 feet, what would be the total area of the floor?

_____

6 Harriet was going to add a round window to her shop. The window would have a circumference of 43.96 inches. What would be the radius of the window?

_____

Name _____ Date _____

10 IS A POWERFUL NUMBER

To multiply decimals by 10, 100, or 1,000, move the decimal point to the right as many places as there are zeros. Sometimes you have to write zeros in the product to move the decimal point the correct number of places.

0.63 × 10: move the decimal point 1 place to the right = 6.3.
0.95 × 100: move the decimal point 2 places to the right = 95.0.
0.335 × 1,000: move the decimal point 3 places to the right = 335.0.
0.7 × 100: move the decimal point 2 places to the right and write a zero in the product = 70.0.

 Read the problem.
Harry bought 10 bags of peanuts at the game. Each bag cost $0.25. What was Harry's total cost for the peanuts?

 Identify the facts.
Each bag of peanuts cost $0.25. Harry bought 10 bags.

 Solve the problem.
Multiply the decimal by the whole number. Use the pattern to move the decimal point. $0.25 × 10 = $2.5 = $2.50 (Add a zero to make the money amount correct.) Harry paid $2.50 for the peanuts.

Now it's your turn! Use the pattern of multiplying decimals by moving the decimal point. Add zeros if necessary.

1. Jesse paid $12.00 for a ticket to the game. If 1,000 people bought tickets at that price, how much money was collected?

   _____

2. Each program cost $2.00. Only 100 people bought a program. How much money was collected for the programs?

   _____

3. Mr. Young bought his scout troop baseball pennants. Each pennant cost $5.00. How much did he spend for 10 pennants?

   _____

4. The teams played an average of 3.5 hours per game. How many hours would they play in 10 games?

   _____

Name _____ Date _____

EVERYTHING IN ITS PLACE!

When you multiply decimals by whole numbers or decimals by decimals, multiply as if both numbers are whole numbers. To place the decimal point in the product, use this pattern: Count the total number of decimal places in the multiplier and multiplicand. You will then have that many decimal places in the product. Sometimes you need to add zeros in the product to place the decimal point correctly.

 Read the problem.

Dad bought a membership to a fitness club for 3.5 months. Each month cost $55.70. How much did Dad pay for the membership?

 Solve the problem.

Multiply the numbers. Count the decimal places in the multiplier and multiplicand. Place the decimal point. When working with money, you should have only 2 numbers to the right of the decimal point. $55.70 a month × 3.5 months = $194.950 = $194.95. Dad paid $194.95 for the membership.

Now it's your turn! Count the number of decimal places to put the decimal point in the correct place. Add zeros if necessary.

1. The club restaurant charges $1.52 for a glass of juice. Each carton holds 4.5 glasses. How much money will the restaurant make with 1 carton of juice?

   _____

2. Members can swim in the pool for 10.5 hours each day. The pool is open 6 days a week. How many hours can members swim in the pool each week?

   _____

3. Each of the 1,000 club members receives an average of 2.5 announcements each month. How many announcements does the club mail each month?

   _____

4. At the club, babysitting costs $5.50 for 1 hour. How much would babysitting cost for 3.5 hours?

   _____

Name _____ Date _____

LET'S BAKE SOME CUPCAKES!

A number sentence shows how numbers relate to each other. Writing a number sentence can help you to solve the problem more easily. Be sure to count the number of decimal places in the multiplier and multiplicand to place the decimal point correctly.

 STEP 1 > **Read the problem.**
A recipe calls for 1.25 cups of flour for 1 dozen cupcakes. If you are baking 2.5 dozen cupcakes, how many cups of flour will you need?

 STEP 2 > **Write a number sentence.**
1.25 cups for 1 dozen × 2.5 dozen = total cups of flour

 STEP 3 > **Solve the problem.**
Multiply the decimals. Count the decimal places to put the decimal point in the correct location. 1.25 × 2.5 = 3.125. You will need 3.125 cups of flour for 2.5 dozen cupcakes.

Now it's your turn! Write a number sentence to help you solve each problem. Round your answers to the nearest 0.5.

1. The recipe calls for 6.33 ounces of milk for 1 dozen cupcakes. How many ounces of milk would you need for 4.5 dozen cupcakes?

_____

2. The recipe also calls for 3.6 ounces of berries for 1 dozen cupcakes. How many ounces of berries would you need for 2.25 dozen cupcakes?

_____

3. You decide to put 0.25 ounces of sparkles on each dozen cupcakes. How many ounces of sparkles would you need for 10.5 dozen cupcakes?

_____

4. Grandma wants to bake 0.5 dozen cupcakes. She needs one-half the amount of ingredients as for 1 dozen cupcakes. How much flour, milk, and berries will she need to bake 0.5 dozen cupcakes? (Hint: multiply each amount for 1 dozen cupcakes by 0.5.)

_____

Name _____ Date _____

WHAT'S IN STORE?

Some problems use more than one operation. List the facts and plan the operations you will use to solve the problem.

STEP 1 ▷ Read the problem.
Mike and Kim worked at the grocery store after school. Mike worked 2.5 hours a day. Kim worked 1.5 times longer than Mike each day. If Kim earned $5.20 an hour, how much would she earn for a day's work?

STEP 2 ▷ Make a plan.
First you must find how many hours Kim worked a day. Multiply. Then you must figure how much Kim earned for a day's work. Multiply again.

STEP 3 ▷ Solve the problem.
2.5 hours Mike worked × 1.5 times longer = 3.75 hours Kim worked each day.
3.75 hours Kim worked × $5.20 an hour = $19.50 a day Kim earned for her day's work.

Now it's your turn! Make a plan to help you solve each problem.

1. Mike stocked shelves at the store. He could put 0.75 of a box of cans on a shelf 1.5 feet long. If he had a shelf 10.5 feet long, how many boxes of cans could he put on it?

   _____

2. How many boxes of cans could he put on a shelf 7.5 feet long?

   _____

3. Kim liked to work in the flower shop at the store. She would wrap each bunch of flowers with 0.6 feet of ribbon. If she had to wrap 12 bunches of flowers, how many feet of ribbon would she use?

   _____

4. If the ribbon cost $0.30 a foot, how much would it cost for Kim to wrap the 12 bunches of flowers?

   _____

LET'S GO TO THE ZOO!

There is a pattern you can use when you divide a decimal by a multiple of 10. To divide a decimal by 10, 100, or 1,000, move the decimal point in the dividend to the left as many places as there are zeros in the divisor.

$0.75 \div 10$: move the decimal point 1 place to the left = 0.075.
$25.9 \div 100$: move the decimal point 2 places to the left = 0.259.
$658.4 \div 1,000$: move the decimal point 3 places to the left = 0.6584.

 Read the problem.
You have 3.5 pounds of peanuts to feed 10 monkeys at the zoo. If you give each monkey an equal amount, how much will each monkey get?

 Solve the problem.
Divide the decimal by the whole number.
Use the pattern to move the decimal point.
3.5 pounds ÷ 10 monkeys = 0.35 pounds
Each monkey gets 0.35 pounds of peanuts.

Now it's your turn! To solve each problem, use the pattern to move the decimal point.

1. The zoo buys 1.25 tons of hay each week to feed 10 elephants. Each elephant eats the same amount of hay. How much hay does each elephant eat in a week?

   _____

2. The zoo has 100 snakes. The snakes eat 15.5 pounds of food each day. If each snake eats the same amount, how much does each snake eat in a day?

   _____

3. The zoo has 1,000 birds in the bird house. The birds eat 675.75 pounds of seed in a week. If each bird eats the same amount, how much seed would 1 bird eat in a week?

   _____

4. The refreshment stand at the zoo sells lemonade. In 100 days, 5,386.5 gallons of lemonade were sold. How many gallons of lemonade were sold each day?

   _____

Name _____   Date _____

WATERMELON, ANYONE?

To divide a decimal by a whole number or a decimal, place the decimal point in the quotient above the decimal point in the dividend. Then divide as you do with whole numbers. Sometimes you need to add zeros in the quotient to line up the decimal points.

 STEP 1 **Read the problem.**
The farmer brought watermelons to the market. He sold 15 melons for $54.75. It cost him $1.12 to grow and harvest each melon. How much profit did he make on the sale of 1 melon?

 STEP 2 **Make a plan.**
First you must figure how much it cost him to grow and harvest the melons. Multiply $1.12 × 15. Then subtract this amount from the amount he made at the market. The difference will be his profit for the sale of 15 melons. Then you must divide his total profit by 15 melons to get his profit on 1 melon.

 STEP 3 **Solve the problem.**
$1.12 × 15 = $16.80 (his cost to grow and harvest 15 melons)
$54.75 − $16.80 = $37.95 (his profit on the sale of 15 melons)

$$\begin{array}{r} \$2.53 \\ 15\overline{)\$37.95} \end{array}$$ The farmer made $2.53 profit on each melon.

Now it's your turn! Solve these problems. When you divide, line up the decimal point in the quotient with the decimal point in the dividend. You can use a calculator to check your answers.

1. You have 2 watermelons. One melon weighs 6.93 pounds, and the other weighs 5.61 pounds. If you cut both melons into slices weighing 0.33 pound each, how many slices can you serve altogether?

_____

2. Watermelons are on sale. You can buy 3 melons for $6.99 at 1 store. Each melon weighs 12 pounds. At another store, watermelons are $0.15 per pound. These melons weigh 12 pounds each, too. Which watermelons are the better buy?

_____

Name _____ Date _____

PARTY TIME!

Some problems do not tell you to add, subtract, multiply, or divide, or how to combine these operations. You must read the problem carefully to choose the operation. In these problems you will have to decide whether to multiply or divide.

 Read the problem.

Twelve children ate birthday cake. Each piece of cake weighed 0.22 pounds. One half the cake is left. How much did the whole cake weigh?

 Choose an operation.

To find how much the whole cake weighed, multiply.

 Solve the problem.

12 pieces × 0.22 pounds per piece = 2.64 pounds = $\frac{1}{2}$ of the cake

2.64 pounds × 2 halves = 5.28 pounds

The whole cake weighed 5.28 pounds.

Now it's your turn! Choose an operation to solve each problem.

1. Guests at the party drank chocolate milk. Each pitcher held 38 ounces. If 12 guests each drank 9.5 ounces of milk, how many pitchers of milk did they drink?

_____

2. One snack at the party was a bag of corn chips that weighed 16.5 ounces. If 15 guests each ate an equal amount, how many ounces of chips did each guest eat?

_____

3. Party favors cost $1.45 for each guest. If there were 17 guests at the party, how much did the party favors cost altogether?

_____

4. Friends ate the remaining 2.64 pounds of cake. It was cut into equal pieces that weighed 0.33 pound each. How many friends ate the remaining cake?

_____

Name _____ Date _____

MATH MADNESS

Harriet the Handy Woman has had lots of different jobs. Help her solve these problems about her job as a delivery driver.

1 For a while Harriet the Handy Woman worked as a delivery driver. Every day she had to drive from the warehouse to the store and back. The round trip was 7.75 miles. If she drove the round trip 10 times a day, how many miles would she drive in a day?

_____

2 How many miles would she drive in 5 days?

_____

3 On one trip Harriet had to deliver 100 boxes that weighed 0.75 pounds each. What was the total weight of her delivery?

_____

4 On another trip Harriet had to deliver 1,000 bottles that each held 0.3 ounces of perfume. How many ounces of perfume did she deliver?

_____

5 On 1 delivery Harriet carried a box that weighed 31.5 pounds. She knew the box held 14 hammers. How much did each hammer weigh?

_____

6 Harriet earned $5.70 an hour as a delivery driver. If she worked 17.5 hours one week, how much money did she earn?

_____

Name _____ Date _____

RATIOS ARE LIKE FRACTIONS

A ratio is a way of comparing numbers or quantities. To figure the ratio, compare the parts to the whole. The ratio is found by dividing one number by another. The ratio is the quotient of the two numbers or quantities. Ratios can be written in several ways. For example, the ratio of 1 thing compared to 2 things can be written as 1 to 2, 1:2, or $\frac{1}{2}$.

 Read the problem.
What is the ratio of triangles to all shapes in this illustration?

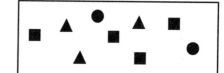

 Identify the facts.
The total number of shapes is 9. The number of triangles is 3.

 Solve the problem.
To find the ratio, divide the number of triangles by the total number of shapes. Reduce your answer if possible.

$3 \div 9 = \frac{3}{9} = \frac{1}{3}$ The ratio is 3 to 9, or 1 to 3. It can also be written as 1:3 or $\frac{1}{3}$.

Now it's your turn! Use the illustration below to find the ratios in each problem. Write the ratios in 3 ways. Reduce your answers if possible.

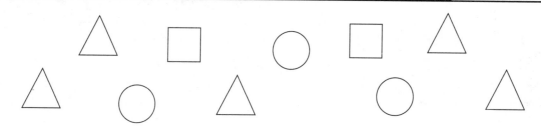

1. What is the ratio of triangles to total shapes?

_____

2. What is the ratio of squares to total shapes?

_____

3. What is the ratio of circles to squares?

_____

4. What is the ratio of circles to triangles?

_____

Name _____ Date _____

ARE THESE THE SAME?

Sometimes you will have two ratios that have the same value. These are called equal ratios. Use cross-products to decide if two ratios are equal. It is logical to conclude that if the cross-products are equal, the ratios are equal.

 Read the problem.

There are 9 coaches for 45 players on the soccer team. What is the ratio of coaches to players? Is $\frac{4}{20}$ an equal ratio?

STEP 2 **Solve the problem.**

First find the ratio of coaches to players. Reduce your answer if possible.

9 coaches to 45 players = $\frac{9}{45}$ = $\frac{1}{5}$

To find if another ratio is equal, multiply both numerators by the opposite denominators. Doing this will give you the cross-products.

Does $\frac{1}{5} = \frac{4}{20}$? $\frac{1}{5} \times \frac{20}{4} = \frac{20}{20}$

The cross-products are equal, so the 2 ratios are equal. $\frac{1}{5} = \frac{4}{20}$

Now it's your turn! Decide if these ratios are equal. To solve the problems, figure the cross-products. Write yes if the ratios are equal or no if they are not equal.

1. Bananas are on sale at 5 for $1.00. Is the ratio of 5 bananas for $1.00 equal to the ratio of 15 bananas for $3.00?

_____

2. Grapes are on sale at $0.69 per pound. Is this equal to 3 pounds of grapes for $2.75?

_____

3. Oranges are on sale at 2 pounds for $0.90. Is this equal to 3 pounds of oranges for $1.35?

_____

4. Apples are on sale for $0.75 per pound. Is this equal to 4 pounds of apples for $2.90?

_____

Name _____ Date _____

LOOK HERE!

Making a table will help you to figure equal ratios more easily.

STEP 1 > **Read the problem.**

Ned went to the mall to rent some videos. He had $6.00. He knew that videos rented for $2 each. How many videos can Ned rent?

videos	1	2	3
cost	$2	$4	?

STEP 2 > **Solve the problem.**

Making a table can help you solve the problem. A ratio table shows equal ratios. If 1 video costs $2, then 2 videos cost $4. How much do 3 videos cost?

$$\frac{1}{\$2} = \frac{2}{\$4} \quad \text{and} \quad \frac{1}{\$2} = \frac{3}{\$6}$$

By multiplying cross-products, you can see that 3 videos would cost $6. Since Ned has $6.00, he can rent 3 videos.

Now it's your turn! Make a ratio table to help you solve each of these problems.

1. Ned also went to the video arcade. It costs Ned $1.00 to play 2 games. How much would it cost Ned to play 10 games?

   _____

2. How much would it cost Ned to play 7 games?

   _____

3. Ned ended up at the music store. CDs were on sale at 2 CDs for $22.00. How much would 6 CDs cost?

   _____

4. How much would 8 CDs cost? _____

5. How much would 1 CD cost? _____

Name _____   Date _____

THIS IS TO THAT

An equal ratio is also called a proportion. Proportions are used to solve problems with equal ratios. Use cross-products to find proportions.

 STEP 1 ▷ **Read the problem.**
Jake can buy 8 apples for $2. How much will 4 apples cost?

 STEP 2 ▷ **Write a number sentence.**
To find how much 4 apples will cost, you multiply to find an equal ratio.

 STEP 3 ▷ **Solve the problem.**
To find an equal ratio, find the cross-products:

$$\frac{8 \text{ apples}}{\$2} = \frac{4 \text{ apples}}{\$?} \qquad 8 \times ? = 4 \times \$2 \qquad 8 \times ? = \$8 \qquad ? = \$1$$

Jake can buy 4 apples for $1.

Now it's your turn! Use proportions and cross-products to find the answers. Write a number sentence to help you solve each problem.

1. Jake can buy 5 oranges for $1. How much would 20 oranges cost?

   _____

2. A dozen pencils costs $0.96. How much does 1 pencil cost?

   _____

3. How much do 6 pencils cost?

   _____

4. Mr. Barnes uses 1 quart of paint to make 4 signs for the store. How many quarts of paint would he need to make 10 signs?

   _____

5. Jake can jog the 2 miles to the store in 30 minutes. How long would it take Jake to jog 3 miles?

   _____

Name _____ Date _____

HOW HIGH IS THAT?

Proportions can be used to find the heights of objects that are too tall to measure easily. Use a formula to help you solve the problem.

 Read the problem.

A 5-meter post casts a 3-meter shadow. A flag pole casts a 15-meter shadow. How tall is the flag pole?

 Use a formula.

Use t to equal the height of the flag pole. Then put the other numbers you know into a formula.

$$\frac{5 \text{ m post}}{3 \text{ m shadow}} = \frac{t}{15 \text{ m shadow}}$$

Solve the problem.

Use cross-products to find the value of t.

$5 \times 15 = 3 \times t$ $75 = 3t$ $\frac{75}{3} = t$ $25 = t$

The flag pole is 25 meters tall.

Now it's your turn! Use a formula and proportions to help you solve these problems.

1. Stu is 6 feet tall. He is standing by a tree. His shadow is 4 feet long. The tree's shadow is 12 feet long. How tall is the tree?

   _____

2. The school building casts a shadow 15 feet long. A traffic sign is 6 feet tall and casts a shadow 3 feet long. What is the height of the school building?

   _____

3. A street light is 7 meters tall. It casts a shadow 2 meters long. A water tower near the street light casts a shadow 8 meters long. How tall is the water tower?

   _____

4. Antoine thought the basketball hoop was too high. It was supposed to be 10 feet high. Antoine was 5 feet tall and his shadow was 3 feet long. The shadow of the hoop was 7 feet long. Was the hoop too high?

   _____

Name _____ Date _____

1 IN 100

The ratio of any number to 100 is called a percent. Percent is written as %.

Percents can also be written as a decimal. Change a percent to a decimal by moving the decimal point 2 places to the left. Drop the % sign.

Change a decimal to a percent by moving the decimal point 2 places to the right. Add the % sign.

Fractions can also be changed to percents. Find an equivalent fraction with 100 as the denominator. Then write the number as a percent.

30 out of 100 = $\frac{30}{100}$ = 30% = 0.30

1 out of 100 = $\frac{1}{100}$ = 1% = 0.01

100 out of 100 = $\frac{100}{100}$ = 100% = 1

7 out of 20 = $\frac{7}{20}$ = $\frac{35}{100}$ = 35% = 0.35

Now it's your turn! Solve these problems.
Write the percentages at least 2 different ways.

1. Seven out of every 10 students wore blue jeans on the field trip. What percent of students wore blue jeans?

   _____

2. What percent of students did not wear blue jeans?

   _____

3. Eight of the 50 people on the bus were parents. What percent of the people were parents?

   _____

4. What percent were not parents?

   _____

5. Three out of 4 students took sandwiches in their sack lunches. What percent of the students took sandwiches?

   _____

6. What percent did not take sandwiches?

   _____

SOME OF YOUR BUSINESS

Percents are used often in business. Stores often have items on sale. The sale price is some percentage off the regular price. The difference in price is called a discount. Governments often charge a sales tax on certain items. The sales tax is added to the price of the item. So knowing percentages can make you a better shopper!

 Read the problem.

Jacy found a bike that was on sale for 25% off the regular price of $80. There was a 6% sales tax on the selling price. What was the total cost of the bike?

 Make a plan.

First find the sale price of the bike. Multiply the regular price by 25% (0.25) and subtract the product from the regular price. Then find the sales tax. Multiply the sale price by 6% (0.06). Then add the sale price and the sales tax to get the total cost.

 Solve the problem.

$80.00 × .25 = $20.00

$80.00 (regular price) − $20.00 (discount) = $60.00 (sale price)

$60.00 × 0.06 (sales tax) = $3.60 (tax)

$60.00 + $3.60 = $63.60   The total cost was $63.60.

Now it's your turn! Solve these problems about percentages.

1. Jacy also bought a bike helmet that was on sale for 20% off the regular price of $39.00. The sales tax was 6%. What was the total cost of the helmet?

   _____

2. The store was having a sale on bike shorts. Jacy found a pair that was 15% off the regular price of $12.00. The sales tax was 6%. What was the total cost of the shorts?

   _____

3. Jacy rode her new bike to the library. On the way she stopped to buy a soda for $0.59. The sales tax was 6%. What was the total cost of the soda?

   _____

4. The library had 3,000 books. Of these, 35% were fiction. How many books were nonfiction?

   _____

5. How many books were fiction?

   _____

MATH MADNESS

When Harriet is not busy on a project, she likes to work in her garden.

1 Harriet has 75 vegetable plants in her garden. Of these, 24% are bean plants. How many bean plants does Harriet have?

_____

2 Harriet has 8 tomato plants and 5 squash plants. What is the ratio of tomato plants to squash plants? Write the ratio 3 ways.

_____

3 What is the ratio of squash plants to tomato plants? Write the ratio 3 ways.

_____

4 Harriet has 8 tomato plants. Of these, 6 are cherry tomato plants. What percentage of Harriet's tomato plants are cherry tomato plants?

_____

5 What percentage of Harriet's 75 vegetable plants are cherry tomato plants?

_____

6 The 8 tomato plants were on sale for $0.30 each. There was also a 7% sales tax. What was the total cost of the 8 tomato plants?

_____

Name _____ Date _____

CHANCES ARE

Probability refers to the chance or likelihood that something will happen. To figure probability, you must first determine the total number of possible outcomes. Then you must compare how likely 1 event is to happen in relation to the total. This comparison is stated as a ratio.

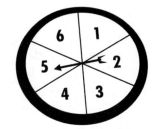

Suppose you are playing a game that uses a spinner. There are 6 numbers on the spinner. You can spin a 1, 2, 3, 4, 5, or 6. That means there are 6 possible outcomes. When you spin, though, you will land on only 1 number. That means there is only 1 happening, or event. Your chance, or probability, of spinning any given number, such as a 2, is 1 chance in 6, or $\frac{1}{6}$.

The chance of the spinner landing on 1 of 2 numbers, such as a 2 or a 3, is the sum of the separate probabilities. The probability of rolling a 2 is $\frac{1}{6}$. The probability of rolling a 3 is also $\frac{1}{6}$. But the probability of rolling a 2 or a 3 is 2 chances in 6, $\frac{2}{6}$ or $\frac{1}{3}$. (Reduce your answer if possible.)

Now it's your turn! Use the drawing of the spinner above to solve these problems.

1. What is the probability the spinner will land on a 6?

_____

2. What is the probability the spinner will land on an odd number?

_____

3. What is the probability the spinner will land on a 1, 2, or 3?

_____

4. What is the probability the spinner will land on a number greater than 1?

_____

TRY YOUR LUCK

| A 1 | B 2 | C 3 | A 4 | B 5 | C 1 | A 2 | B 3 | C 4 | A 5 |

Suppose you are playing a game that uses 10 cards. Each card has a number and a letter on it. Because there are 10 cards, there are 10 possible outcomes. What is the probability you will pick a card with an A or 1?

probability of picking an A = $\frac{4}{10}$ or $\frac{2}{5}$
probability of picking a 1 = $\frac{2}{10}$ or $\frac{1}{5}$
probability of picking A or 1 = $\frac{2}{5} + \frac{1}{5} = \frac{3}{5}$

Now it's your turn! Use the drawings of the cards above to solve the following problems. Reduce your answers if possible.

1. What is the probability you will pick a card with a B?

   _____

2. What is the probability you will pick a card with a 5?

   _____

3. What is the probability you will pick a card with an odd number?

   _____

4. What is the probability you will pick a card with a B or a 3?

   _____

Name _____ Date _____

WHAT COLOR IS YOUR BACKPACK?

Probability is sometimes called relative frequency. A table makes it easier to show the ratio of the probable events to the total number of outcomes.

Lucy did a survey. She asked her classmates what color backpack they had. She put the results in a frequency table.

There are 30 students in Lucy's class, so there are 30 possible outcomes.

Color	Number of students
blue	8
red	5
black	4
green	7
gray	6

Now it's your turn! Use the table above to solve these problems. Reduce your answers if possible.

1. What color of backpack is the most popular?

    _____

2. What color of backpack is the least popular?

    _____

3. What is the probability that Karen has a red backpack?

    _____

4. What is the probability that Armando has a gray backpack?

    _____

5. What is the probability that Shenille has a green or a black backpack?

    _____

6. What is the probability that Larry does not have a blue backpack?

    _____

WHAT'S YOUR FREQUENCY?

To find the relative frequency, or probability, of an event, write the ratio of the frequency of the event to the total number of possible outcomes.

For a school survey, Josh asked 50 of his classmates how many pets they owned. He put the results in a frequency table.

What is the probability a student owns 4 pets?

probability of 4 pets = $\frac{1}{50}$

Pets Owned	
Event	Frequency
0 pets	5
1 pet	18
2 pets	20
3 pets	6
4 pets	1
Total	50

Now it's your turn! Use the table above to solve these problems. Reduce your answers if possible.

1. What is the probability a student owns 2 pets?

   _____

2. What is the probability a student owns 3 pets?

   _____

3. What is the probability a student owns 2 or 3 pets?

   _____

4. What is the probability Bill has no pets?

   _____

5. What is the probability Karen owns fewer than 4 pets?

   _____

6. What is the probability Alvin owns more than 1 pet?

   _____

Name _____ Date _____

WHAT'S YOUR PREDICTION?

You can use relative frequencies to make predictions.

Josh added a column of relative frequencies to his table. Now he can use the relative frequencies to make predictions.

To predict how many out of 100 students own 3 pets, he wrote a formula, called a proportion, and solved it.

$\frac{n}{100} = \frac{6}{50}$

$n \times 50 = 6 \times 100 \qquad n \times 50 = 600 \qquad n = 12$

Pets Owned		
Event	Relative Frequency	Frequency
0 pets	5	$\frac{1}{10}$
1 pet	18	$\frac{9}{25}$
2 pets	20	$\frac{2}{5}$
3 pets	6	$\frac{3}{25}$
4 pets	1	$\frac{1}{50}$
Total	50	1

Now it's your turn! Use the table and proportions to make predictions.

1. How many out of 100 students own 2 pets?

    _____

2. How many out of 100 students own 2 or 3 pets?

    _____

3. How many out of 200 students own 1 pet?

    _____

4. How many out of 100 students own fewer than 4 pets?

    _____

5. How many out of 500 students own 1 pet?

    _____

BATTER UP!

The study of statistics deals with collecting, organizing, and analyzing mathematical facts, or data. You see statistics everywhere you turn, especially in elections and sports. Using a number sentence can help you to figure statistics more easily.

One important term in statistics is *average*. Sports statistics use a player's average in many categories. An average is usually figured by dividing the number of successful attempts by the total number of attempts.

For example, a baseball batting average is the number of safe hits (successful attempts) divided by the number of times at bat (total number of attempts). A 0.300 batting average is the same as 30% and means the hitter gets 30 hits in 100 times at bat, or 300 hits in 1,000 times at bat.

30 hits ÷ 100 at-bats = 0.300 batting average
300 hits ÷ 1,000 at-bats = 0.300 batting average

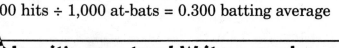

Now it's your turn! Write a number sentence to help you find the averages for these problems.

1. Sal had 45 hits in 180 at-bats. What is his batting average?

   _____

2. Sara had 50 hits in 150 at-bats. What is her batting average?

   _____

3. In 12 baseketball games, Shana made 22 free throws in 33 tries. What is her free-throw shooting average?

   _____

4. The school soccer team has played 12 games and won 7. What is the team's winning average?

   _____

5. Jane is the pitcher on the softball team. In 5 games, she pitched to 175 batters and struck out 75 of them. What is Jane's strike-out average?

   _____

Name _____ Date _____

WHAT DO YOU THINK?

You have probably heard about surveys and polls. Surveys and polls ask a selected number of people, called a sample, some questions. Because a poll cannot really ask 10 million people what they think, the poll will ask 1,000 people and then project the results to the larger group.

The sample can be random, meaning there is no real order to the choosing of the people. Or the sample can be scientific, meaning the poll asks representative people.

Food	Girls	Boys
Pizza	7	8
Hamburger	5	4
Taco	5	6
Hot Dog	3	2

For example, you want to conduct a lunchroom poll about favorite foods. You could use a random sample, where you ask every third or fourth student what he or she likes to eat. Or you could use a scientific sample, where you ask an even number of boys and girls.

You decide to ask 20 girls and 20 boys in the sixth grade what their favorite food is. You put the results in a table.

Now it's your turn! Use the table and proportions to project, or predict, results for larger groups.

1. If 7 out of 20 girls like pizza, how many girls out of 100 would probably like pizza?

_____

2. If 6 out of 20 boys like tacos, how many boys out of 200 would probably like tacos?

_____

3. If 5 out of 40 boys and girls like hot dogs, how many boys and girls out of 120 would probably like tacos?

_____

4. If 20 out of 40 boys and girls like hamburgers and tacos, how many boys and girls out of 400 would probably like hamburgers and tacos?

_____

Name _____ Date _____

MATH MADNESS

Harriet likes problems about probabilities and statistics.
Help her solve these problems.

1 Harriet's friend Barry did not study for his true/false test. What is the probability he will get the first question right?

_____

2 There are 10 questions on the true/false test. What is the probability Barry will get any 1 question right?

_____

3 Harriet is rolling a die in a board game. The die is a cube with 6 faces, each with a number from 1 to 6. Harriet needs to roll a 5. What is the probability that Harriet will roll a 5?

_____

What is the probability that Harriet will not roll a 5?

_____

4 Harriet likes baseball. She knows that Cy Young was the winningest pitcher in the history of professional baseball. He won 511 games and lost 313. What was his winning average?

_____

5 Cy Young played for 21 years, from 1890 to 1911. What was the average number of games he won each year during that period? Round your answer to the nearest whole number.

_____

6 Harriet played softball for her church team. She was a good batter. One season she got 96 hits in 246 times at bat. What was Harriet's batting average?

_____

What was Harriet's average for not getting hits?

_____

Name _____ Date _____

WHAT SHAPE ARE YOU IN?

Geometry is the mathematics of shapes. Triangles are 3-sided shapes with 3 angles. The sum of the 3 angles is 180 degrees.

Hint: The symbol for degrees is °.

Now it's your turn! Read the description of each kind of triangle. Then label the drawing with the correct type of triangle.

Equilateral triangles have 3 equal sides and 3 equal angles. Isosceles triangles have 2 equal sides and 2 equal angles. Scalene triangles have 3 unequal sides and 3 unequal angles. Right triangles have 1 angle of 90°. Obtuse triangles have 1 angle greater than 90°.

1.

  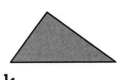

1a. _____   1b. _____   1c. _____

1d. _____   1e. _____

Complete the description of each type of triangle. Either circle the correct answer or fill in the blank.

2. In an equilateral triangle, each angle is _____°.

3. In a right triangle, the sum of the 2 smaller angles is _____°.

4. In an obtuse triangle, the sum of the 2 smaller angles is (greater, less) than 90°.

5. Draw a triangle. Label what kind of triangle it is.

Name _____ Date _____

WHAT'S IN THE CORNER?

Quadrilaterals are 4-sided figures. The sum of the 4 angles in a quadrilateral is 360°.

Now it's your turn! Read the description of each kind of quadrilateral. Then label the drawing with the correct type.

Rectangles have 4 right angles of 90° each. In a rectangle, opposite sides are equal and parallel. Squares are rectangles with 4 equal and parallel sides. Parallelograms have opposite sides that are equal and parallel. Rectangles and squares are parallelograms, but not all parallelograms are rectangles or squares. Trapezoids have no 90° angles. In a trapezoid 1 pair of opposite sides is equal and not parallel. The other pair of opposite sides is unequal and parallel.

1.

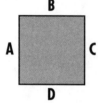

1a. _____

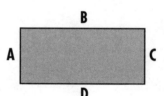

1b. _____

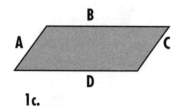

1c. _____

1d. _____

Use the drawings above to complete the description of each type of quadrilateral. Circle the correct answer or fill in the blank.

2. In the rectangle, 2 parallel sides are (A, C or C, D).

3. In a square, the sum of 2 opposite angles is _____.

4. In the parallelogram, 2 sides that are equal and parallel are (A, C or B, C).

5. In the trapezoid, the sides that are unequal and parallel are (B, D or A, C).

6. Draw a quadrilateral and label what type it is.

Name _____ Date _____

AREA CODE

You can find the perimeter and area of any geometrical shape using a formula. The perimeter is the sum of the length of the sides. The area is the total space. The area is expressed in square units, such as square inches.

A = Area   P = Perimeter   W = Width   H = Height
S = Side   B = Base (the bottom of a triangle)

Rectangle: To find the perimeter, use the formula P = 2W + 2H.
    To find the area, use the formula A = W × H.
Square: To find the perimeter, use the formula P = S × 4.
    To find the area, use the formula A = S × S or A = W × H.
Triangle: To find the perimeter, use the formula P = S + S + S.
    To find the area, use the formula A = $\frac{1}{2}$ B × H.

STEP 1 > **Read the problem.**
    Find the area of this rectangle.

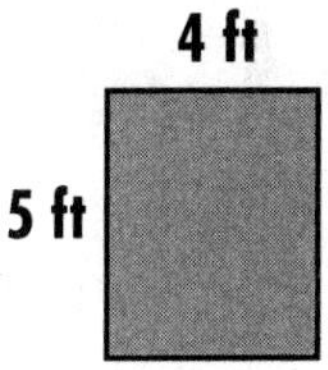

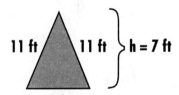
4 ft
5 ft

STEP 2 > **Choose a formula.**
    To find the area of a rectangle, use the formula A = W × H

STEP 3 > **Solve the problem.**
    A = W × H   A = 4 feet × 5 feet   A = 20 square feet

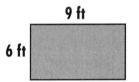
9 ft
6 ft
figure 1

6 ft
6 ft
figure 2

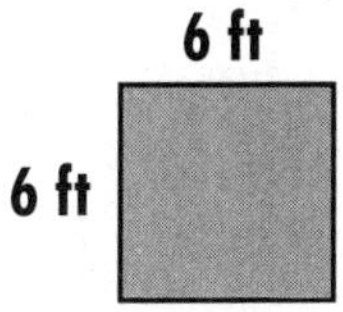

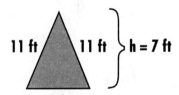
11 ft   11 ft   } h = 7 ft
7 ft
figure 3

✏ **Now it's your turn! Use the formulas and drawings above to find the area and perimeter of each shape.**

1. Figure 1: Area = _____   Perimeter = _____
2. Figure 2: Area = _____   Perimeter = _____
3. Figure 3: Area = _____   Perimeter = _____
4. Draw a rectangle, square, or triangle. Label it with dimensions.
    Then find the area and perimeter of your shape.

Name _____ Date _____

ROUND AND ROUND WE GO!

To find the circumference of a circle, use the formula C = πD. In the formula, D is the diameter of the circle. The diameter is a line between two points on the circumference, or the outer edge of a circle. The diameter passes through the center of the circle. The π in the formula is equal to 3.14.

To find the area of a circle, use the formula A = πr². The radius, or r, is the distance from the center of the circle to the circumference. The radius is equal to $\frac{1}{2}$ of the diameter.

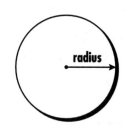

HINT—The little 2 by the r means to square the number, or multiply it by itself.

 Read the problem.
Find the circumference and area of a circle with a diameter of 8 inches.

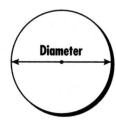

 Identify the facts.
The circle's diameter is 8 inches.

 Use a formula.
To find the circumference of a circle, the formula is C = πD.
To find the area of a circle, the formula is A = πr².

STEP 4 **Solve the problem.**
To find the circumference:
π = 3.14   D = 8   C = 3.14 × 8 = 25.12
The circumference is 25.12 inches.

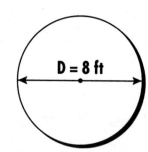

To find the area:
π = 3.14   r = $\frac{1}{2}$ × D = $\frac{1}{2}$ × 8 = 4   r² = 4 × 4 = 16
A = 3.14 × 16 = 50.24
The area is 50.24 square inches.

Name _____ Date _____

ROUND AND ROUND
WE GO, PART 2

Now it's your turn! Use a formula and make a drawing to help you solve these problems.

1. The diameter of a circle is 18 inches. What is the radius?

   _____

2. A wheel has a diameter of 14 inches. What is the circumference of the wheel?

   _____

3. An apple pie has a radius of 5 inches. What is the area of the pie?

   _____

4. If you cut the pie into 8 pieces, what part of the circumference will each piece be?

   _____

5. A circle has a radius of 6 inches. What is the circumference?

   _____

6. A circle has a diameter of 16 inches. What is the area of the circle?

   _____

7. A small pizza has a diameter of 8 inches. A large pizza has a diameter of 14 inches. What is the difference in area between the large pizza and the small pizza?

   _____

8. A tabletop has a circumference of 188.4 inches. What is the radius of this round tabletop?

   _____

Name _____ Date _____

PROBLEMS WITH THE THIRD DIMENSION!

A three-dimensional figure has width, depth, and height. An example is a box. On a rectangular box, there are 6 surface areas, or faces. The top and bottom are the same size in area, the front and back are the same size, and the remaining 2 sides are the same size. To find the total surface area of the box, you must find the area of the top, the front, and a side. Add these areas, then multiply by 2 to find the area of all 6 faces.

 Read the problem.
Find the total surface area of a rectangular box with these dimensions in inches:
W = 4; H = 2; L = 3.

 Make a plan.
First you must find the area of the top, the front, and a side. Then add the 3 areas. Then multiply by 2.

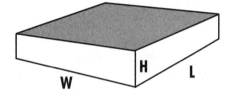

STEP 3 **Solve the problem.**
Find the areas.
Top A = 4 × 3 = 12 square inches
Front A = 4 × 2 = 8 square inches
Side A = 3 × 2 = 6 square inches
Add the areas.   12 + 8 + 6 = 26 square inches
Then multiply by 2.   26 × 2 = 52 square inches.
The rectangular box has a total surface area of 52 square inches.

Now it's your turn! Make a plan, then solve these problems.

1. A rectangular box is 8 inches wide, 10 inches long, and 4 inches high. What is the total surface area of the box? _____	**2.** A square box (also called a cube) has a height of 5 inches. What is the total surface area of the cube? _____

Name _____ Date _____

HOW MUCH IS IN THERE?

Volume is the amount of space inside a three-dimensional object. Volume is measured in cubic units, for example, cubic inches.

To find the volume of a rectangular box, use the formula
$V = W \times L \times H$.

 Read the problem.
What is the volume of a rectangular box with these dimensions in inches: W = 4; L = 3; H = 2?

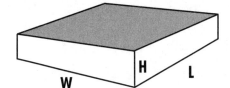

 Use a formula.
To find the volume of a rectangular box, the formula is $V = W \times L \times H$.

 Solve the problem.
$V = 4 \times 3 \times 2 = 24$. The volume of the box is 24 cubic inches.

Now it's your turn! Use a formula to solve these problems.

1. A square box (cube) has a width of 4 inches. What is the volume of the cube?

   _____

2. A rectangular box has a height of 6 inches, a width of 10 inches, and a length of 7 inches. What is the volume of the box?

   _____

3. A cube has a height of 7 inches. What is the volume of the cube?

   _____

4. A small shed has a width of 10 feet, a length of 12 feet, and a height of 8 feet. What is the volume of the shed?

   _____

MATH MADNESS

One day Harriet decided to do some math problems about shapes and objects. Help Harriet to solve these problems. Use the correct formula from the list below.

To find the area of a rectangle, use the formula A = W x H.
To find the perimeter of a rectangle, use the formula P = 2W + 2L.
To find the circumference of a circle, use the formula C = πD.
To find the area of a circle, use the formula A = πr .
To find the volume of a rectangular box, use the formula V = W x L x H.

1 Harriet had a sheet of plywood in her shop. It was 8 feet long and 4 feet wide. What was the area of the plywood?

_____

2 Harriet had a box that was 6 inches high, 10 inches wide, and 12 inches long. She had 750 cubic inches of sawdust to put in the box. Would all the sawdust fit in the box?

_____

3 What was the volume of Harriet's box?

_____

4 Harriet wanted to put a round pond in her backyard. She had picked out a spot that was 12 feet wide and 12 feet long. She designed a pond with a circumference of 34.54 feet. Would the pond fit in the spot Harriet had picked?

_____

5 What was the area of the spot Harriet had selected?

_____

6 What was the area of the pond Harriet had designed?

_____

Name _____ Date _____

BOTH SIDES ARE THE SAME

Most math problems give you all the numbers you need to solve the problem. Some problems do not give all the numbers. These problems have an unknown, also called a variable.

Algebra is a kind of mathematics that uses variables. These variables are part of an equation. An equation is like a formula. In an equation, the values on 1 side of the equal sign are the same as the values on the other side. Because the values are the same, you can solve the equation to find the variable.

 Read the problem.

Cal has 27 models. Of these, 12 are model ships.
The rest are model airplanes. How many airplanes does Cal have?

 Write an equation.

The unknown number is how many airplanes Cal has. This unknown number, or variable, is usually called X. An equation to find X can be written in 2 ways. One way uses addition: 12 ships + X airplanes = 27 models. A second way uses subtraction: 27 models − 12 ships = X airplanes

Now it's your turn. Write 1 addition and 1 subtraction equation for each problem. You do not have to solve the equations.

1. Cal has 12 model ships. Of these, 5 are aircraft carriers, and the rest are cruisers. How many cruisers does Cal have?

_____

2. Cal also likes to collect coins. He has 38 old coins. Of these, 21 are dimes, and the rest are pennies. How many pennies does Cal have?

_____

3. Cal has 21 dimes in his coin collection. Of these, 16 are Roosevelt dimes, and the rest are Liberty dimes. How many Liberty dimes does Cal have?

_____

4. Cal also collects stamps. He has 43 foreign stamps. Of these, 18 are from England. The rest are from Mexico. How many Mexican stamps does Cal have?

_____

Name _____ Date _____

X MARKS THE SPOT!

Equations can also use multiplication and division. Even though the operations are different, multiplication and division equations are written the same way. You still need to find the variable.

 STEP 1 > **Read the problem.**

Susan had 20 cookies. She gave an equal number of cookies to each of her 5 friends. How many cookies did Susan give each friend?

STEP 2 > **Write an equation.**

The variable is how many cookies Susan gave each friend. The equation to find the variable, X, can be written in 2 ways.

One way uses multiplication:

5 friends × X cookies each = 20 cookies

A second way uses division:

20 cookies ÷ 5 friends = X cookies each

or   20 cookies ÷ X cookies each = 5 friends

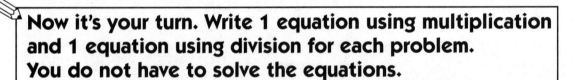

Now it's your turn. Write 1 equation using multiplication and 1 equation using division for each problem. You do not have to solve the equations.

1. Susan made 24 sandwiches for the picnic. She made an equal number of 3 different kinds of sandwiches. How many of each kind did she make?

   _____

2. Susan made 24 sandwiches for the picnic. She put an equal amount of sandwiches in 6 sacks. How many sandwiches did Susan put in each sack?

   _____

3. Susan bought 36 cans of soda for the picnic. She bought an equal number of cola, root beer, and orange sodas. How many cans of each kind did she buy?

   _____

4. Susan brought 28 treats to the picnic. She had an equal amount of cookies, cupcakes, granola bars, and crackers. How many of each kind of treat did she bring?

   _____

Name _____ Date _____

WHAT IS X?

When you solve an equation, you must find the value of the unknown number, or variable.

 Read the problem.

Jenny has 22 CDs. That is 5 more than Maria has. How many CDs does Maria have?

 Write an equation.

Let X = the number of CDs Maria has. You can use either addition or subtraction to write the equation.

     X CDs Maria has + 5 more = 22 CDs Jenny has

or   22 CDs Jenny has − 5 more = X CDs Maria has

 Solve the equation.

To solve for X, you must get X alone on 1 side of the equal sign.

    X + 5 = 22   X + 5 − 5 = 22 − 5   X = 17

or   22 − 5 = X   17 = X   Maria has 17 CDs.

Now it's your turn. Write an equation using addition or subtraction for each problem. Then solve each equation. (Hint: Let X = the variable.)

1. Maria has 17 CDs. Of these, 9 are rock music, and the rest are pop music. How many pop music CDs does Maria have?

    _____

2. Maria has 17 CDs. This is 14 fewer CDs than her friend Lewann has. How many CDs does Lewann have?

    _____

3. Lewann wants to see her favorite band. Tickets cost $15 each. This is $4 more than Lewann has. How much money does Lewann have?

    _____

4. Lewann's dad says he will give Lewann the extra money if she will wash dishes 20 days in the next month. This is 3 days more than she already washes the dishes. How many days does Lewann wash the dishes now?

    _____

Name _____ Date _____

MORE EQUATIONS TO SOLVE

Equations can also be solved using multiplication and division. Again, you must find the value of the variable.

 Read the problem.

Jason wants to buy a new video game that costs $30. This is 2 times the amount of money Jason has. How much money does Jason have now?

 Write an equation.

Let X = the money Jason has now. You can write an equation using either multiplication or division.
X money Jason has × 2 times more = $30 cost of game
or $30 cost of game ÷ 2 times more = X money Jason has

 Solve the equation.

You must get X alone on 1 side of the equal sign.
$X \times 2 = \$30$ $X \times \frac{2}{2} = \frac{\$30}{2}$ $X \times 1 = \$15$ $X = \$15$
or $\$30 \div 2 = X$ $\$15 = X$ Jason has $15 now.

Now it's your turn. Write an equation using multiplication or division for each problem. Then solve each equation. (Hint: Let X = the variable.)

1. In Jason's video game, he has to solve a problem about a rectangular room before he can leave it. The area of the room is 180 square feet, and it has a width of 15 feet. What is the length of the room? (Remember the formula: Area = length × width.)

    _____

2. In another part of the game, Jason is trapped in a circle. To escape he must find the diameter of the circle. The circumference of the circle is 40.82 feet. What is the diameter of the circle? (Remember the formula: Circumference = π × diameter.)

    _____

3. Jason must solve a final problem before he can finish the game. The Red Gorp has 72 shots left. This is 3 times as many shots as the Blue Gorp has left. How many shots does the Blue Gorp have left?

    _____

4. At the end, Jason has scored 96 points. His score is 3 times better than Kyle's best score. What is Kyle's best score?

    _____

Name _____ Date _____

GET TOGETHER!

You know that in addition and multiplication you don't have to work the problem in any special order. The numbers $4 + 5 + 6$ can also be added as $6 + 5 + 4$, and the sum both ways is the same. The numbers $3 \times 4 \times 5$ can be written as $5 \times 3 \times 4$, and the product will be the same.

But when multiple operations are included, order is important. The problem $4 \times 5 + 2$ is not the same as the problem $4 + 2 \times 5$. To keep numbers organized in equations, parentheses are used.

 Read the problem.
$X = 4(5 + 2) - 2(3 - 1)$

 Make a plan.
First add and subtract the numbers in the parentheses. The 4 and 2 beside the parentheses mean to multiply those numbers by the number in the parentheses. Finally, subtract to find X.

 Solve the problem.
$X = 4(5 + 2) - 2(3 - 1)$
$X = 4(7) - 2(2)$ $X = 28 - 4$ $X = 24$

Now it's your turn! Write an equation to solve each problem. Be sure to group your functions using parentheses.

1. Kay has 24 trading cards. Kent has twice as many less 4. How many cards does Kent have?

_____

2. In July Kent got 2 paychecks for $85.00 each. He had to pay 3 bills of $50.00 each. How much money did Kent have left?

_____

3. Kay took a test in math. Each correct answer was worth 5 points. Each wrong answer counted off 4 points. Kay had 17 correct answers and 3 wrong answers. What was her final score?

_____

4. At the end of August, Kay had $80.00. Kent had 3 times as much less $15.00. How much money did Kent have at the end of August?

_____

Name _____ Date _____

INTO THE UNKNOWN!

You have learned how to solve equations with a single unknown or variable. But some equations have more than 1 variable. And sometimes the variable has a beginning value greater than X.

 Read the problem.

At the basketball game, floor seats cost $3 each and bleacher seats cost $2 each. Your class buys $70 worth of tickets, with 10 more bleacher seats than floor seats. How many of each type of ticket does the class buy?

 Write an equation.

Let X = floor seats.

$3X + $2(X + 10 more bleacher seats) = $70

Solve the equation.

First do the arithmetic. $3X + $2(X+10) = $70

$3X + $2X + $20 = $70

Now get all the variables on 1 side of the equal sign and all the known numbers on the other side. Remember to change signs when you move from 1 side of the equal sign to the other side.

$5X + $20 − $20 = $70 − $20 $5X = $50   X = $\frac{$50}{$5}$ X = 10

Your class buys 10 floor seats and 20 bleacher seats.

Now it's your turn! Write an equation for each problem. Then solve the equation.

1. Find this number. This number added to 4 times this number equals 15. Call this number X. What is the value of X?

_____

2. Here's another number to find. The value of 3 times this number minus 6 equals 2 times this number plus 6. Call this number X. What is the value of X?

_____

3. Mr. Allen took his family to the movies. Tickets were $7 for adults and $4 for children. He gave the clerk $30 and received $8 in change. How many of each ticket did Mr. Allen buy?

_____

Name _____ Date _____

MORE OR LESS?

Sometimes equations are not equal. These unequal equations are called inequalities. Inequalities do not use the equal sign. Instead, they use the "greater than" sign (>) and the "less than" sign (<). Hint: the point of these signs always aims at the smaller number.

 Read the problem.

Together Sandra and Nadene have less than 20 movie posters. Sandra has 4 more posters than Nadene. How many posters might Nadene have?

 Write an inequality.

Let X = Nadene's posters.
$X + (X + 4) < 20$

 Solve the inequality.

$X + (X + 4) < 20$
$2X + 4 < 20$ $2X < 20 - 4$ $\frac{2X}{2} < \frac{16}{2}$ $X < 8$
Nadene has fewer than 8 posters.

Now it's your turn! Write an inequality and then solve each problem.

1. The value of X plus 3 is greater than 12. What might the value of X be?

   _____

2. Find the value of X: 10 times the value of X plus 7 is less than 47. What is the value of X?

   _____

3. Together Nick and Raul scored more than 40 points in a basketball game. Nick scored 6 more points than Raul. How many points might Raul have scored? (Hint: Let X = Raul's score.)

   _____

4. Carol and Conrad together have less than $50. Carol has $10 more than Conrad. How much money might Conrad have?
   (Hint: Let X = Conrad's money.)

   _____

5. How much money might Carol have?

   _____

MATH MADNESS

One evening Harriet was sitting by her backyard pond. She was thinking about all the math she had learned recently. Help Harriet review by solving these problems.

1 In her job as a delivery driver, Harriet had worked a total of 97.5 hours. She had earned $5.70 an hour. How much were her total earnings from her delivery job?

_____

2 Harriet's garden had done well. She had harvested $7\frac{1}{4}$ pounds of squash and $8\frac{2}{3}$ pounds of beans. How many total pounds of these vegetables did she harvest?

_____

3 Harriet's tomatoes also did well. She harvested $10\frac{1}{2}$ pounds of tomatoes. She gave $\frac{1}{3}$ of these to her neighbors. How many pounds of tomatoes did she give to her neighbors?

_____

4 Harriet admired the flowers in her garden. She had 12 yellow flowers and 9 red flowers. What was the ratio of red flowers to yellow flowers?

_____

5 Harriet was planning to build a square shed in her backyard. If the floor size was 8 feet by 8 feet, what would be the total area of the floor?

_____

6 Harriet was going to add a round window to her shop. The window would have a circumference of 43.96 inches. What would be the radius of the window?

_____

7 Harriet looked at the sky. The weather report had predicted a 25% chance of rain. What was the probability it would rain?

_____

8 Harriet had 2 final projects to build. She knew that one project would use 2 times as many nails as the other. She had 120 nails. How many nails could she use in each project?

_____

Assessment
P. 12
1. about 2,000 spangles
2. no
3. Megan won.
4. yes
5. 2-1/8 pages
6. 4-1/3 laps

P. 13
7. 3/8
8. 1-1/4 ounces
9. 21 smaller servings. ~~He used 3 3/4 cups of gravy in his goulash.~~
10. 0.67575 pounds
11. 3 pitchers
12. $5.00
13. yes

P. 14
14. 18 feet
15. 11 in 30 or 11/30
16. 0.250
17. 103.62 square inches
18. 64 cubic inches
19. Equations will vary. Maria has 8 pop music CDs.
20. Raul scored more than 17 points.

Whole Numbers
P. 15
1. about 2,000 spangles
2. about 7 pages
3. about 800 miles
4. about 1,600 miles

P. 16
1. 13 decorations
2. 52 free tickets
3. 32,376 kernels
4. 9 pairs

P. 17
1. 6 hours
2. yes
3. no
4. $19.00

P. 18
1. 675 x 33 ÷ 75 = 297
2. 210 x 3 − 321 + 4 = 313
3. 195 + 3 x 4 ÷ 24 − 5 = 28

P. 19
1. 7,285 people vanished
2. 3,760 people remained
3. no
4. 21 postcards

P. 21
1. Miami
2. Austin
3. 11,000 T-shirts
4. 22,000 T-shirts
5. $33,000.00
6. $66,000.00
7. $242,000.00

P. 22
1. 0
2. Possible answers. Some answers may vary.
   a. 2 ÷ 2 x 2 ÷ 2 = 1
   b. 2 − 2 x 2 + 2 = 2
   c. 2 x 2 + 2 ÷ 2 = 3
   d. 2 x 2 x 2 ÷ 2 = 4
   e. 2 ÷ 2 + 2 + 2 = 5
   f. 2 x 2 x 2 − 2 = 6
3. Possible answers. Some answers may vary.
   a. 3 + 3 + 3 ÷ 3 = 3
   b. 3 x 3 + 3 ÷ 3 = 4
   c. 3 + 3 ÷ 3 + 3 = 5
   d. 3 + 3 x 3 ÷ 3 = 6
   e. 3 ÷ 3 + 3 + 3 = 7

Fractions
P. 23
1. 4 shirts
2. 4/16 or 1/4
3. 2 dresses
4. 2/10 or 1/5
5. 10 pairs
6. 10/30 or 1/3

P. 24
1. 1/6 more dinosaur toys
2. 4/7 were yo-yos.
3. 8/12 or 2/3
4. 4/12 or 1/3
5. 4/9 are monsters.

P. 25
1. Megan won.
2. Jimmy ran farthest.
3. Mary won.
4. Katie won.

P. 26
1. bottoms
2. 8/9 of a roll
3. 1/9 of a roll
4. 5/8 of the bows were used.
5. 3/8 of the bows were left.
6. 3/7 had gold ribbon.

P. 27
1. 2/12 or 1/6 of a sheet
2. yes
3. 11/12 of a bag
4. 1/12 of a bag left

P. 29
1. 46 feet of wood
2. 10-foot counter and 4-foot counter
3. 154 feet
4. 90/154 or 45/77
5. 48/154 or 24/77
6. 16/154 or 8/77
7. two 8-foot counters and one 4-foot counter
8. 10-foot counters = 48/64 or 3/4; 4-foot counter = 16/64 or 1/4

P. 30
1. 1/4 of a pie
2. none
3. Harriet: $10,000.00; brother: $6,000.00; sister: $4,000.00
4. yes
5. 5/6 of a yard for $4.50

Improper Fractions
P. 31
1. Both are same size.
2. On Tuesday they used more fuel.
3. Both worried same amount.
4. Thom spent more time.

P. 32
1. no
2. 172/5 units
3. 33/4 units
4. 67/4 units

P. 33
1. second day
2. 17/8 or 2-1/8 pages
3. Planet Z was closer.
4. 1/15 light-year

P. 34
1. Second landing spot was closer.
2. 1/8 space mile
3. 4-5/12 liters
4. Second tank held more.
5. 2-9/10 units
6. 37-1/10 units

P. 35
1. Thom collected more.
2. 1/8 pound more
3. 7-4/10 or 7-2/5 hours
4. 2-4/10 or 2-2/5 hours longer
5. 13/16 pound

P. 36
A. 1/2
B. 5/12
C. 3-7/13
D. 9-5/9
E. 1/4
F. 1-1/2
G. 9/16
H. 10
I. 3/4
J. 2-1/2
K. 1/10
L. 15-5/28
M. 7/8
N. 1-1/3
O. 7/9
P. 1
Q. 2-1/20
R. 10-7/12
S. 4-3/16
T. 3-7/12

P. 37
Magic Gates are:
G, E, C, R, N, F, S

P. 38
1. 2-3/5 boxes
2. country: 25; rock: 40; hip-hop: 35
3. 4-11/12 cans
4. 8-5/12 feet

Multiplying Fractions
P.39
1. 4 arrows
2. 32 free throws
3. 60 strikes
4. 40 balls

P. 40
1. 4/15 of the mail
2. 44 letters
3. 97 letters
4. 70 magazines donated
5. 42 magazines used for scrapbooks

P. 41
1. 7/16 cup bleach
2. 1/4 cup pepper
3. 6 cups broth
4. 39 people

P. 42
1. 1-2/5 miles
2. 4-1/3 laps

P. 43
1. 3/8 of the flour
2. 5/8 of the flour
3. 5-1/8 pounds
4. 2-9/16 pounds
5. 12-13/16 pounds

P. 44
1. 6-1/4 cups water
2. 2-1/3 teaspoons of garlic salt

P. 45
1. 24 seconds
2. 210 seconds
3. 1-1/6 minutes faster

P. 46
1. 1/2
2. 4
3. 25
4. 48
5. 24
6. 12
7. 6
8. 2/3
9. 2/3
10. 1,234
11. 1,234
12. 1,234

Dividing Fractions
P. 47
1. 384 salespeople
2. 24 badges
3. 20 quarters

P. 49
1. 2/9 of the files
2. 1/4 dozen
3. 3 donuts
4. 1/6 of a gallon
5. 5/24
6. 5 pieces

P. 50
1. 1-1/4 ounces
2. 1-5/6 dozen
3. 22 flowers
4. 4/5 sheet

P. 51
1. 38 smaller meatballs. ~~He bought 2 pounds of beef.~~
2. 30 slices. ~~She used 1/2 cup of nuts and 3/4 cup of honey in her recipe.~~

P. 52
1. 15 casts
2. 8 bandages
3. 6 days
4. 26 packages

P. 53
1. Ruben: 5/6 ÷ 1/5 = 5/6 x 5/1 = 25/6 = 4-1/6
   Milly: 4/6 ÷ 1/5 = 4/6 x 5/1 = 20/6 = 3-2/6 or 3-1/3
   Chan: 3/6 ÷ 1/5 = 3/6 x 5/1 = 15/6 = 2-3/6 or 2-1/2
   Rosa: 2/6 ÷ 1/5 = 2/6 x 5/1 = 10/6 = 1-4/6 or 1-2/3
   Skip: 1/6 ÷ 1/5 = 1/6 x 5/1 = 5/6 = 5/6

Answer Key

© Steck-Vaughn Company

P. 54
1. $555.75
2. 15 -11/12 pounds
3. 3 -1/2 pounds
4. 3 to 4
5. 64 square feet
6. 7 inches

Decimals
P. 55
1. $12,000.00
2. $200.00
3. $50.00
4. 35 hours

P. 56
1. $6.84
2. 63 hours
3. 2,500 announcements
4. $19.25

P. 57
1. 28.5 ounces
2. 8 ounces
3. 3 ounces
4. 0.5 cup flour; 3 ounces milk;
   2 ounces berries

P. 58
1. 5.25 boxes
2. 3.75 boxes
3. 7.2 feet
4. $2.16

P. 59
1. 0.125 ton
2. 0.155 pound
3. 0.67575 pound
4. 53.865 gallons

P. 60
1. 38 slices
2. melons for $0.15 per pound

P. 61
1. 3 pitchers
2. 1.1 ounces
3. $24.65
4. 8 friends

P. 62
1. 77.5 miles
2. 387.5 miles
3. 75 pounds
4. 300 ounces
5. 2.25 pounds
6. $99.75

Ratios and Percentages
P. 63
1. 1 to 2, 1:2, 1/2
2. 1 to 5, 1:5, 1/5
3. 3 to 2, 3:2, 3/2
4. 3 to 5, 3:5, 3/5

P. 64
1. yes
2. no
3. yes
4. no

P. 65
1. $5.00
2. $3.50
3. $66.00
4. $88.00
5. $11.00

P. 66
1. $4.00
2. $0.08
3. $0.48
4. 2.5 quarts
5. 45 minutes

P. 67
1. 18 feet
2. 30 feet
3. 28 meters
4. yes

P. 68
1. 70%, 70/100
2. 30%, 30/100
3. 16%, 16/100
4. 84%, 84/100
5. 75%, 75/100
6. 25%, 25/100

P. 69
1. $33.07
2. $10.81
3. $0.62 or $0.63
4. 1,950 nonfiction books
5. 1,050 fiction books

P. 70
1. 18 bean plants
2. 8 to 5, 8:5, 8/5
3. 5 to 8, 5:8, 5/8
4. 75%
5. 8%
6. $2.57

Probability
P. 71
1. 1 in 6 or 1/6
2. 3 in 6 or 1 in 2, 3/6 or 1/2
3. 3 in 6 or 1 in 2, 3/6 or 1/2
4. 5 in 6 or 5/6

P. 72
1. 3 in 10 or 3/10
2. 2 in 10 or 1 in 5, 2/10 or 1/5
3. 6 in 10 or 3 in 5, 6/10 or 3/5
4. 2 in 5 or 2/5

P. 73
1. blue
2. black
3. 5 in 30 or 1 in 6, 5/30 or 1/6
4. 6 in 30 or 1 in 5, 6/30 or 1/5
5. 11 in 30 or 11/30
6. 22 in 30 or 11 in 15,
   22/30 or 11/15

P. 74
1. 20 in 50 or 2 in 5, 20/50 or
   2/5
2. 6 in 50 or 3 in 25, 6/50 or
   3/25
3. 26 in 50 or 13 in 25, 26/50
   or 13/25
4. 5 in 50 or 1 in 10, 5/50 or
   1/10
5. 49 in 50 or 49/50
6. 27 in 50 or 27/50

P. 75
1. 40
2. 52
3. 72
4. 98
5. 180

P. 76
1. 0.250
2. 0.333
3. 0.667
4. 0.583
5. 0.428 or 0.429

P. 77
1. 35
2. 60
3. 15
4. 200

P. 78
1. 1 in 2 or 1/2
2. 1 in 2 or 1/2
3. 1 in 6 or 1/6, 5 in 6 or 5/6
4. 0.620
5. 24 games
6. 0.390, 0.610

Geometry
P. 79
1a. equilateral
1b. isosceles
1c. scalene
1d. right
1e. obtuse
2. 60
3. 90
4. less
5. Answers will vary.

P. 80
1a. square
1b. rectangle
1c. parallelogram
1d. trapezoid
2. A, C
3. 180°
4. A, C
5. B, D
6. Answers will vary.

P. 81
1. A = 54 square feet;
   P = 30 feet
2. A = 36 square feet;
   P = 24 feet
3. A = 24 square feet;
   P = 28 feet
4. Answers will vary.

P. 83
1. 9 inches
2. 43.96 inches
3. 78.5 square inches
4. 3.925 inches
5. 37.68 inches
6. 200.96 square inches
7. 103.62 square inches
8. 30 inches

P. 84
1. 304 square inches
2. 150 square inches

P. 85
1. 64 cubic inches
2. 420 cubic inches
3. 343 cubic inches
4. 960 cubic feet

P. 86
1. 32 square feet
2. no
3. 720 cubic inches
4. yes
5. 144 square feet
6. 94.985 square feet

Pre-Algebra
P. 87
Possible answers. Equations
may vary.
1. 5 + X = 12; 12 − X = 5
2. 21 + X = 38; 38 − X = 21
3. 16 + X = 21; 21 − X = 16
4. 18 + X = 43; 43 − X = 18

P. 88
Possible answers. Equations
may vary.
1. 3 x X = 24; 24 ÷ X = 3
2. 6 x X = 24; 24 ÷ X = 6
3. 3 x X = 36; 36 ÷ X = 3
4. 4 x X = 28; 28 ÷ X = 4

P. 89
Equations will vary.
1. Maria has 8 pop music
   CDs.
2. Lewann has 31 CDs.
3. Lewann has $11.00.
4. Lewann washes dishes
   17 days a month now.

P. 90
Equations will vary.
1. The length is 12 feet.
2. The diameter is 13 feet.
3. Blue Gorp has 24 shots
   left.
4. Kyle's best score is 32.

P. 91
Equations will vary.
1. Kent has 44 cards.
2. Kent has $20.00 left.
3. Kay's final score was 73.
4. Kent had $225.00.

P. 92
1. X = 3
2. X = 12
3. 2 adult and 2 children
   tickets

P. 93
1. X > 9
2. X < 4
3. Raul scored more than
   17 points.
4. Conrad has less than
   $20.00.
5. Carol has less than $30.00.

P. 94
1. $555.75
2. 15-11/12 pounds
3. 3-1/2 pounds
4. 9 to 12 or 3 to 4; 9/12
   or 3/4
5. 64 square feet
6. 7 inches
7. 1 in 4 or 1/4
8. 80 nails and 40 nails